CHINESE
LANTERNS

Lynne,
To warm your soul
and tickle your
inner child —

Best
Margie Hiermer

MARGIE HIERMER

www.eigramm.com
PO Box 44794
Columbus, OH 43204

Chinese Lanterns
by Margie Hiermer

First Printing – July 2016
Paperback ISBN: 978-0-9973334-0-4
eBook ISBN: 978-0-9973334-1-1
Library of Congress Control Number: 2016934298
Cover design by Columbus Publishing Lab
Some cover source material provided by:
vectoropenstock and freevector
Back cover photo by Talitha A. Tarro

This is a work of nonfiction. The events and experiences detailed herein have been faithfully rendered to the best of my ability. Though conversations come from my or others' keen recollection of them, they are not always written to represent word-for-word documentation.

Printed in the U.S.A.

For Loany

CONTENTS

CHAPTER 1

Paradise Rice

*"Does anyone know how far down a metal
detector will go?"*

—1975

Eighteen slot machines are buried in the hillside overlooking the confluence of the Big and Little Darbys in Georgesville, Ohio. The slate grey house at the top sits vacant now, aging in silent testimony to the grandeur it once displayed and the secret it has kept since the early fifties when Aunt Loany stashed them there.

Back then, the lawns were manicured precisely with garden bouquets bursting from flower beds surrounding the home. Blue and white striped metal awnings topped each window and shaped the roof to a two-story porch that ran the length of the house. Wrought iron railing and open air on the second floor, the porch was decorated with edgy metal glass tables and overstuffed chairs, more for enjoying hors d'oeuvres and a martini than a serious blackjack or poker game.

Situated underneath, the downstairs porch featured an enclosed Florida room with jalousie windows, coconut shrunken heads, and fan palms adorning the walls. Conch shells and other sea creatures rested on driftwood end tables topped in glass. An aqua and green carpet runner stretched the length of the room, a stark contrast to the pale yellow walls and brown tweed wrought iron couches that lined it. At both ends of the room stood doorways—one led to a drive-under garage and boathouse—the other into a guest room and then on to an entertaining kitchen and party room.

Knotty yellow pine walls welcomed visitors into the space. Tan and brown floor tiles were arranged in a central four square with one shade offset by a defining border of the other to provide continuity and purpose. Reversing the color pattern of each bold geometric design gave the room a feeling of expansiveness and endless possibility. Shiny white metal cabinets, kitchen appliances with chrome accents, and recessed fluorescent lighting reflected onto the knotty pine and occupied the wall between the party room, garage, and boathouse. The contrast between the man-made slick, clean, and hard materials faded into the warm, rich wood tones and overstuffed comfortable furniture, offering balance along with variety.

This was a room of contradictory faces—banquet preparation, dressing area, private poker parties, and at times, a short-term bank vault to count and hide more cash than most any common man could ever imagine seeing in one place at one time. Here, there was something for everyone.

From either porch, guests could gaze out over the hillside hiding the slot machines to the dam Okie Rice built to create his water paradise. A footbridge led to a concrete and earthen island in the center of the Little Darby—low dive on the shallow side by the wooden plank footbridge—high dive and ski boat moored across the way, ready for any takers. Oversized, brass tiki torches and smudge pots lit the island and the night grounds, beckoning like a lighthouse to guide the pontoon boat back home. Ever present was the gentle sound of water spilling over the dam, and if one listened closely the whispers of the envious and petty local area critics bubbling up from the foam and spray might be heard. *"Okie's folly. This is Okie's folly."*

Okie tackled a large amount of the work himself on the dam even though he didn't really know what he was doing; but this pretty much characterized how he and Loany approached most every project. Both had a "Just Do It" steel constitution interlaced with unwavering faith. Had Nike existed back then and been without principle and scruples, the Rices would have been their "go-to" representatives—because Okie and Loany surely knew how to create extreme wealth from illegal business ventures.

Since the Rices owned roughly fifty acres on both sides of the creek, they could do virtually anything they wanted, and they did. An avid hunter and fisherman his entire one hundred years of life, Okie first bought a rowboat and stuck it on the muddy Little Darby, followed by a ten-horsepower motor that ended up too big for the tiny hull. That was when Loany and Okie decided to erect the dam. And the island. Then they added a ski boat; and then a pontoon boat. Eventually, thirteen Cadillacs joined their stable of toys. In addition, they constructed and maintained a regulation baseball park on the far side of the Little Darby.

AMVETS Field hosted big city league play and tournaments all season long on the Rice's property. Evening games began with a full military color guard and presentation of the flag, complete with lighting, concession stands, dugouts, and a public address system. The field popped out suddenly to an unsuspecting traveler winding down sleepy Alkire Road and discovering it for the first time, a bit out of place among the stands of hearty oaks and gently rolling farm land filled with cornfields and cattle pastures resting on the western border of Franklin County.

On the other side of the main grounds, across the road, were two modest houses and a ten-stall stable assigned over the years to protect and house the Rices' various relatives and beloved racehorses. Pasture land sloped down from the stable and spilled into the Big Darby. A metal storage building bounded the back of the property alongside a railroad track and trestle that rose fifty feet above and spanned the Big Darby.

The pedestrian entryway to Paradise Rice was flanked on one side by a life-size clay donkey and sombrero-clad Mexican statue. On the other side, a black-faced, ceramic stable boy dressed in white jockey pants and red riding jacket extended an arm and held a glowing lantern. A stone-and concrete-capped curb framed the property along Alkire Road, turning abruptly and rising into a waist-high wall to divide the lawn and paved driveway tarmac. The wall opened to four steps and a walkway, followed by four more leading to the front porch entry, all topped again with the familiar blue and white awning. The stone wall continued past the walkway as it grew to head height and curved around to border the drive-under garage.

Above the basement and garage towered the main floor of Paradise Rice, a ramble shack and hodgepodge of rooms with no rhyme or reason. The house started out as a three-room shanty pulled onto the site after Loany found out the property was for sale. And then as Loany would have ideas, and as the money came, they just kept adding on. First came an enlarged living room, new kitchen, and another bedroom. Next they added a serving room and dining room, and finally, narrow but ample seating rooms with continuous windows that defined two outer walls of the house. Gazing east, the view followed along Alkire Road, up the hill toward the Oak Grove Tavern, and to the west, past Goldhardt's Grocery. These were great views, and not simply for aesthetic purposes. The vast panorama gave them the ability to watch for the law in case a raid had been planned for Paradise Rice.

Inside the main house, the furnishings could be described with words other than common or predictable. Paradise Rice was a mix of racehorse and Polynesian, with a touch of the Southwest, the Far East, and everything else mixed in. This was Loany's self-inspired country estate, and back then, money was no object. Rich French provincial furniture crowded the bedrooms, barely leaving the subtle stripe of the Southwestern inspired carpet pattern visible. More traditional, but always very expensive, furniture adorned the remaining common area. Luxurious seating sofas followed and curved along the outline of each room. An Italian marble coffee table filled with a ceramic milking lady and her swans cohabitated with brass duck lamps and a leather shaded floor lamp. A pair of ceramic clowns guarded the fireplace standing post on the mantel along with an antique clock Loany's family brought over from Germany. *Lladrós,* Hummel figurines, glassware, and other relics were scattered around tables, windowsills, and the hearth.

Like the lower level of Paradise Rice, all the walls except in the bedrooms and bath were constructed of knotty pine and framed in high-gloss white woodwork. These walls were cluttered with an eclectic collection of artifacts and seemingly unrelated objects—though if any theme emerged, the animal and bird kingdom edged out other subject matter. A pair of leather carved horse pictures in wood frames finished off a living room wall. A wool handwoven likeness of White Socks, a pacing pony Loany adopted to live out his days at Paradise Rice, was prominently displayed above the sideboard in the dining room. An Asian-style parrot painting, a pair of iron white and gold peacocks, glass sconces, and tooled metal art decorated the walls. Custom-made, silk-lined draperies in a flowered pattern with neutral linen sheers framed the endless windows, portals designed to invite the outside in throughout the house. But, wide metal blinds covered the serving room windows and allowed inside activity to be hidden from the world whenever necessary. One large oval portrait was visible from the main entry, that of Loany and her son, Jerry.

Directly beyond the serving room sat one of Loany's most prized possessions, a cylinder *carte* music box originally handcrafted before 1900 for the owner of the Union Pacific Railroad. It had been custom-made for his invalid daughter and included her favorite songs. A local mining engineer and prosperous man in his own right eventually acquired the piece and presented it to Loany as thanks for all she had done for his daughter Georgia, a woman among Loany's lifelong and dearest of friends. It was an enormous gift both in meaning and value, bestowed simply because "nice" does end up mattering to some people.

The music box was so elegant and substantial, it required its own display table. The piece could have easily doubled as a small child's coffin, though its destiny was meant to celebrate the joy of lifelong friendships, not the sorrow of an early death. Both the music box and table were handcrafted of rosewood with inlaid designs of African exotics in light and medium tones. The table contained a drawer that held five steel tube-shaped cylinders, each of which played four complete songs on a 144-note comb. The lid on the music box tilted open from the front. Inside a glass top protected the inner mechanics and cylinder along with eight separate bell chimes. A heavy-duty, double spring drove the cylinder, and a ratchet style, wind-up handle was tucked into one end of the wood case.

The sound was irresistible whatever the song or moment, regardless of a listener's personal taste. "Polonaise," "The Blue Danube," "March of the Toy Soldiers," and similar songs resonated stridently from within the box and invariably attracted a group of fascinated admirers whenever in play. The melodies that drifted out from within the music box were such a contrast to the driving hard rock of electric guitars we usually listened to or the big band sounds of brass Loany favored.

She never minded if we kids played the music box, even though its value most likely would have been appraised at over one hundred thousand dollars. Loany cherished it indeed, but as a treasure to share, use, and enjoy. It did not sit on display behind velvet roping or bulletproof glass in a museum room where kids absolutely were not welcome. For Loany, possessions could be replaced or lived without altogether—even a one-of-a-kind masterpiece like the Union Pacific owner's music box. Assets of the material world were easily acquired and appreciated, then moved around, given away, or discarded. A piece might start out prominently displayed on the main floor of Paradise Rice and then be moved to a bedroom or relegated to the basement sun porch to make room for the new thing *du jour*.

Loany cleaned her mother's house just like she cleaned her own, and after leaving there, Mom was routinely spotted out at the trash pile retrieving all the items that had been thrown away that day—a coffee grinder, wooden step stool, or an assortment of glassware. This back and forth purging and salvaging ritual was one that flourished between the two women and continued for decades. Loany carted stuff out; Mom hauled it back to the house. Loany returned there and threw more treasure on the heap. Mom waited until the coast was clear and dragged it all back inside.

But the music box was one possession that did not make the journey to Loany's trash pile. It simply rested along a wall easily within reach where it could have been bumped, scratched, kicked, or spilled on. It remained in the same spot for fifty years at Paradise Rice and was never damaged in any way.

The music box drew visitors into the serving room and beyond twenty years after Loany had stashed the slot machines in the hillside. Inevitably, everyone stopped by to visit when they passed by the house. Visitors frequently came and went, throughout the day and night, be they relatives, business associates, friends or the bevy of adopted misfits Loany collected throughout her life. Whether staying for a long while or just a few minutes, all were fussed over, coddled and made to feel like they were the most important people in the world. At that moment, nothing mattered more than their particular story or their particular tale of trouble or woe. Loany invariably took the time to stop and listen and to intently focus on the minutest of details from her visitors' saga. She cackled along with them and often made them laugh at an absurd escapade of her own.

Being around Loany made one feel like a million bucks, even when life's slot machines had sent a soul severely hemorrhaging into the red, be it financially or emotionally. A visit with Loany gave a reprieve from the worries of the day and put a fresh face on the world if even just for that short time. It was for all her special brand of an elixir, a fix that intoxicated, addicted, and guaranteed you returned for more. More Loany time, to make things right.

Perhaps the morning had brought Loany the honor of being escorted by the police from a busy downtown street, where she had window-shopped from the car while inching along happily at her leisure, snarling traffic to a standstill. Or maybe that afternoon she had refused to be run off the Big Darby by a work crew of burly Darby Dan farmhands. Standing up defiantly and wobbling side to side in a canoe, she let them know in no uncertain terms that the guns they held did not scare her one bit, nor did they own the water, damn it.

* * *

Whenever a group of Loany's nieces and nephews happened to descend on her at the same time, a discussion of the slot machines eventually filtered into our group talk. That the eighteen slot machines were entombed in the hillside was pretty much accepted as fact by all. Together we dreamed of digging them up to keep as souvenirs and to split the booty between us. How totally cool would we be to have a slot machine to show our friends? A slot machine absolutely trumped a homemade go-kart or dune buggy.

Over the years, we had whispered among ourselves and pieced together sufficient information about Loany and Okie's un-Christian past to confirm the existence of said coveted hardware.

In the mid-twentieth century, the underground one-armed bandit business worked much like that of its respectable aboveboard cousin—the snack vending machine—with the not insignificant exception that purchasing a Coke or Snickers with coin was, and remains, completely legal. Either a person owned the slot machine, stocked it, maintained it and collected all the money, or he allowed a vendor to place the equipment on premises and then received a percentage cut of the earnings. Since Loany and Okie fancied diversification, they used both strategies.

The *why* of the slot machines being stuck in the hillside was a bit fuzzier and really quite irrelevant to the actual extraction. The *why* did provide supplementary intelligence about the slot machines' existence, but that matter had long since been validated between us, so the tale became one in a lineup of fuzzy, overlapping half-stories and rumors about the things Okie and Loany had supposedly done while they were notorious racketeers.

I, for one, *was personally sure* Loany had told me she got wind of an impending raid, just like she always had received advance warning from friendly law enforcement insiders. Except that fateful time, eighteen slot machines happened to rest tucked inside the boathouse waiting for relocation out into the field. She had no time to conjure up a solution, and since the raid occurred during the time the dam was being erected, there were large pieces of earth-moving equipment sitting around the property. So, Loany just had the machines stashed in the hillside. Years later, I would learn it was neither one of the frequent raids nor nearly such an exotic and dangerous tale that sent the slots to their grave. It was simply a change in the gambling laws and a strong desire to keep Okie out of the federal penitentiary.

On this particular day, my brother and a couple of cousins sprawled out across the seating couches next to the music box. We routinely revisited the minutes of our previous discussions, which were just adolescent musings on how to bag the slot machines. Of utmost concern was the timing of the extraction. Should we dig during the day or at night? If we executed our mission well, it would look like a new drain or septic system was being installed, and that way we could work right out in the open. *Hmmmmm.* Nighttime offered more privacy in a way, but lighting our operation could attract unwanted visitors, too. Hey, what if we used a tarp and stretched it up across a wood frame to form a canopy? Back and forth we talked over tired and worn out ideas while grasping for the thing, the perfect plan, we had yet to discover. Eventually, we settled on digging during the day and then coming back to take the slot machines out of the hillside late at night.

Of even more consequence than timing was the actual location of the slot machines. The hillside was hundreds of feet long and practically as wide as it sloped down to the Little Darby, so poking around with a shovel was a ridiculous proposition, not to mention the attention we might draw. Would my dad help us, someone mused? Well, I had seen pictures of him as a young man, tanned and in a T-shirt sitting on top of a bulldozer and moving large boulders about that formed the foundation of the concrete dam. I dunno, for all I knew, he stuck them in the hill for Loany.

There was no way, though, I told my brother, that Mom and Dad were going to let us keep an illegal slot machine—ever. We could just forget it. Having kept us and them sheltered and apart from the Rices' dirty money and dirty pleasures, I did not see owning gambling memorabilia going over too terribly well, particularly since gambling was a sin and breaking the law a definite no-no. The thought of working as hard as we were surely going to and then not being able to keep the treasure was far too much to rectify in our minds, so we simply ignored the thought and moved on. Those were dragons to slay for another day after we nabbed the treasure.

Couldn't we use a metal detector? I mean, with a pile that big they'd be easy to locate...but, wait a minute—the eighteen slot machines could be deep, possibly ten or fifteen feet back in the hill. "Does anyone know how far down a metal detector will go?" My brother scanned the group hoping for an answer.

Of course, eventually the delicate subject of how to divide up the slot machines had to be broached. The obvious solution was to split them up amongst us four ways, though the math didn't work out right. But then, it only seemed right that Okie's grandkids should get in on the action, too, and Loany's granddaughter Pam definitely should receive one. We stalled when we began trying to count through Okie's family and got to his son Perry.

"Does anyone know how many kids he has—is it five or six?" I asked. "Oh crap, you guys, it doesn't look like we have enough to go around."

We gave up trying to decide who we should bestow the treasure on and got back to the fundamentals of location, location, location.

"Why don't we just ask Loany?" a cousin suggested. "She has to know where they are."

We all laughed at the thought. How often had she lost her bifocals when they were hanging right around her neck? It was true. Countless hours had been spent by recruits rummaging through drawers, cars, looking on windowsills, combing through every room in the house only for Loany to find them hidden in the crack of her extremely generous chest and chained around her neck. I mean, we are talking about Loany here, right? It was accurate to say that at times she couldn't even have found her ass to contemplate whether there was a hole in the ground.

"I know right where they are," Loany said with a precisely measured cadence and conviction. There was no anger in her voice, but there was intent to convey with great certainty she was indeed serious, as serious as Loany ever got, anyway.

We had rather forgotten about her at this point. She busied herself in the kitchen while listening to us fools plan our heist, as she prepared food for Okie's upcoming birthday celebration. From time to time, she laughed to herself, shook her head, or chimed in with us. But, she didn't try to steer the conversation or make a judgment about our ideas and dreams. Loany had plenty of opinions and was not the least bit shy about sharing them—but she was capable of being an observer, too.

Yet hearing now from us the notion she might have no idea where the slot machines were located was the deciding point for her to jump off the sideline and join our merry fantasy. Loany stepped down out of the kitchen and made her way into the serving room while licking the spoon she was using to transform a bowl of boiled potatoes into homemade German potato salad.

"Where?" We almost nearly shouted in unison. "Will you tell us?" She had our complete, utter, and undivided attention.

"No." It was a simple one word answer, yet coming from Loany it shocked us.

Seeing our surprise and the undoubtedly deflated faces circling her, she went on to explain that the federal statute of limitations extended over twenty-one years, and it wasn't a matter of *if* but a certainty Okie *would* go to prison should they be uncovered.

"But when would twenty-one years be over?" we had to ask. Members of the extraction group began to squirm now, shifting weight from one foot to the other or pacing back and forth between the window overlooking the hillside and our sacred circle.

Loany held the potato salad spoon frozen in mid air, absently looking far away as if lost inside an old black and white movie of her life from long ago. After a moment, she turned back toward us and said, "Soon. Pretty soon."

This whole statute of limitations thing was unsettling new data for us bandits to take in. Loany's revelation was indeed a setback for us, but certainly not one we couldn't endure. We had dreamed and talked about digging up the slots for years, and if it meant waiting for a while longer, even a couple of years, well, then we would simply do it.

Our collective minds' eyeballs and talk turned now to contemplating the buckets of quarters, dimes, and other coinage we would surely harvest from those eighteen slot machines. Those coins would be well over twenty years old and solid silver to boot. A number of them clearly had to be in collectable mint condition after sleeping undisturbed in their tomb for all those years.

"Can you imagine how much the money will be worth that's in them?" a cousin wondered out loud.

I nodded in agreement, thinking of the coin collection tucked under my bed in an old box and the partially filled albums of pennies, nickels, dimes, and quarters. I had found only three silver coins in all the years I'd sorted through my dad's pocket change or rummaged through the tips I earned from the sweat equity that comes while waiting tables. The silver coins were so worn and dinged up; the dates were barely visible and the relief images of those honored were terribly distorted. Our moods and spirits were shifting back toward the positive. But Loany was about to sucker punch us.

"Do you kids think I left the money in them?" Loany's eyes lit up in a smile now, the lines in her tanned face lifting upward. "*Hey-ell no,*" she added, as she tried to choke back the snorts escaping her throat and nose. "Jesus Christ," Loany blurted out, bursting into laughter as she turned and headed back to the kitchen.

We stood quietly in our circle looking at one another. Now what? *Loany took the flipping money out of them? I can't even believe it.* My mind screamed inside my head as I struggled to accept this bad breath of reality, a possibility we had not even entertained during all our scheming. But, without silver coins buried in them, our sustainable interest in the whole project pretty much ended. So, on that sunny summer day in 1975, the great slot machine extraction mission died forever, at least from my posse of two-arm bandits.

From time to time after that, as we gathered together at Paradise Rice, one of us would broach the topic and breathe a puff of new air into it. But, the conversation never really went anywhere. Of course, the slot machines themselves, even without money, were certainly a part of the appeal, a deliciously dirty and dangerous treasure to have and hold from Loany's past. Theoretically, they should have been reason enough to press on. But nothing ever came of our mission after that.

I thought about those slot machines whenever the occasion brought me to that hillside at Paradise Rice. I wondered what life was like back when the Rices were dodging the law.

CHAPTER 2

The Ballad of Okie and Leona

"You have six months to live."
—Charles Mayo

By the time Leona Mae Goldhardt Dillon was thirty-three years old, she had buried two sisters and a brother-in-law and become a World War II widow—all within the span of roughly four years. Loany was the pet name that had followed her as long as anyone can remember, but the origin of the label remains a mystery to those still living. Grandkids, nieces, and nephews called her Loany. Spouses called her Loany. Friends and bosses called her Loany. Loany simply fit her.

She cared more about her sister Margaret than anyone else in the family, and that death came first in her string of crises and remained one of the hardest Loany ever faced. That the two of them were so close was peculiar, because the two were such a contrast of style and being. Faded black and white pictures of Margaret reveal an old-fashioned, somewhat frumpy woman in plain dress and hat, usually clutching a purse while staring into the camera. Rarely was there a smile on her face. Color photography would not likely have softened her look of dissatisfaction or improved her overall presentation. Serious and solemn, this woman reeked of needing a good stiff drink, or at the very least, a change of venue. Apparently, she hated the camera, so at least there is one more thing we share besides having the same name.

As my namesake and the grandmother I never knew, others knew Margaret in life as the kindest and the most gentle of souls. Steady and reserved, her position in the family was that of the central and calming force, the person who quietly went about her business in the background, cementing a family together—in this case Ollie and Gwenzora Goldhardt's clan of five children. Margaret was the oldest and next in line was Loany, followed by Ruth, then Don, and finally Maxine, as the baby of the group. As is characteristic of clan conduct, this particular family of German hillbillies located and remained for life, in or close to, their native birthplace of Georgesville, Ohio.

Now, Loany, in contrast to Margaret, did quite enjoy the camera and her likeness in its pictures mirrored the person she was—out in the world at ease, sure, and happy, flashing a full and wide set of teeth, her eyes dancing with joy below platinum-bleached hair. She was as equally comfortable posing in a designer gown as barefoot in bib overalls, always barefoot, when dressed casually at home.

Loany had little trouble finding a party with good stiff drinks that she could be the absolute life of, flaunting her New York sense of fashion and style while dripping in jeweled accessories. Most likely, she was surrounded by a host of suitors unanimously hoping to get lucky. Loany simply did not get hung up on what anyone else thought and had no interest in wasting time to combat rumors about her character, be they true or untrue. She flouted tradition and took an unconventional stance toward the particularly "white bread" mores of the 1940s. Loany unequivocally accepted everybody and assumed the rest of the world was open and reasonable in its thinking as she.

Why, didn't everyone have a gay hairdresser as a best buddy back then? Jackson was hers in the years after the big money came, a tall, red-headed and slightly paunchy man who held court with his curlers and tints in the basement salon of the regal Neil House Hotel. Jackson adored Loany and opened up his shop after hours, only for her and her entourage. For, when Loany got her hair and nails done, she absolutely had to have company tag along. The evening became an event of magnificent proportion which included not only the beautification process, but also prime rib dinners for all ordered from the hotel dining room.

Jackson and his dashing and dreamy partner Bob became permanent fixtures on Loany's circuit, visiting Paradise Rice often. They were on hand at stepdaughter Martha's wedding, which ended up being fortuitous: Jackson saved the day and salvaged Loany's dress when the zipper ripped, unable to contain her expansive cleavage; and Bob stepped up and volunteered to sing when it looked like the scheduled entertainment might be a no-show. Later in life, Loany stepped up to console Jackson when Bob dumped him to marry a woman, but not before Bob graduated from, and had dental school financed by, Jackson. Somehow I just cannot imagine Margaret hanging out with a gay hairdresser, no matter how fine-looking his partner Bob was.

Nevertheless, the one thing Margaret and Loany did share in common was working at F & R Lazarus and Company, founder of national retail giant Federated Stores, in the six-story flagship building that dominated the downtown landscape of Columbus, Ohio for decades. Lazarus was a full-service department store of the grandest proportion, a place to get lost in forever and ever. Going to Lazarus simply was a memorable event, one worthy of being saved and nurtured for always. There were furs and gowns, a beauty parlor, and a spa. The jewelry and makeup area sprawled back through the entire first floor toward the

Colonial Tea Room, one of nine restaurants in the building. Full of mirrors and glass, tile and glamour, the Town Street entrance with its promise of beauty and elegance greeted shoppers from across the Midwest. Toyland filled nearly the entire sixth floor and had to be where Santa *really* lived with his elves and reindeer. The furniture department spanned the fifth floor. Grand pianos were on display in the music department along with drums, guitars, brass instruments, and violins. The fine millinery department clothed the rich and locally famous who could conveniently trot across the aisle and finish off that new ensemble with a hat from the hundreds on display, or buy an LP record, or even visit the sporting goods department. There was a petting zoo for the kids, and tucked in among this assortment of finery was department after department of clothes for every shopper's size and budget.

Loany would have moved easily among the glitz and glamour of the F & R Lazarus fortress, unfazed by those individuals in power or of high title, and certainly unapologetic about her position of commonality. So, she had no problem marching right down to the company clinic on the day she learned Margaret had been there all morning, sick. One look told her Margaret needed much more than the company hospital could provide, and Loany demanded to know what was being done. Why was it now lunchtime and she was just finding out about this situation? They knew the two of them were sisters, for heaven's sake.

The company doctors tried to reassure her, but Loany wasn't buying it. One didn't need a medical degree to know her sister was very, very ill. She continued to press, to insist, to badger, and did not let up until they agreed to transport Margaret to the hospital.

Though Loany's instincts were correct, the intervention came too late to save Margaret's life. Before the day was over, she would die from complications of a tubal pregnancy. And, although no one might have been able to save Margaret's life, Loany still blamed herself anyway. She felt there was more she could have done, that she should have been there to take care of Margaret. Her death would shape how Loany took charge of, and managed, the medical community for the next sixty-odd years. Margaret died, but there would be other loved ones who wouldn't because of the care Loany personally gave and for the quality of the medical care she insisted on. Be it by hell raising, constant pestering, or staying on-site around the clock, she kept doctors and nurses in check.

"I said I want a doctor in here now," she once demanded to a nurse standing just beyond Loany's outstretched hand as she poked a crooked index finger wildly through the air. Loany's assertive example reminded us to never, ever forget who the client is and who is paying whose salary.

In her sister Ruth's case, it wasn't that care came too late but rather that no cure was available. Ruth already had been diagnosed with ovarian cancer and would lose the fight fewer than eighteen months after Margaret's death.

When Margaret's husband Wesley decided to sign up to serve in World War II, it sent shock waves through the family. No one expected him to go; he wasn't required with a young boy at home to rear. But Wesley said he just felt like he had to serve—it was the least he could do for his country. They'd taken Loany's husband Pete, and everyone knew he had bad asthma. It just didn't seem right for him to stay home with Pete in Europe fighting. Wesley was emphatic about serving his time. His time on earth ended around Christmas Day in 1944 during the Battle of the Bulge, one of World War II's deadliest campaigns, along with more than one hundred thousand other soldiers.

With Margaret, Ruth, and Wesley's deaths, Loany's position as keeper of the clan became deeply and permanently solidified. She had her own life with a husband and child. But, of particular immediacy, was seeing to the three orphans who were products of all this death—Margaret and Wesley's only child Ron (my father), and Ruth's two children Jim and Judy, whose father was alive but remained mostly missing in action from their lives.

**

Okie Lane Rice knew all about being the responsible one. Born in 1903 on the one hundred year anniversary of the state of Ohio, he had his beginnings farther south in Blaine, Kentucky just over the holler, along Greasy Ridge, not far from the town of Friendly. Okie would not officially become a Buckeye until a teenager when his family made their way to Madison County in a Model T Ford in search of a better life.

Even as a kid, Okie worked hard at most anything he could find to help out his family. After heavy rains saturated the cemetery grounds and carried coffins down a hillside, he lugged them back up with a rope. It was nasty, dangerous, and especially risky work because these particular coffins belonged to those who died from the 1918 Spanish Influenza, the most lethal flu pandemic ever that eventually killed half a million people worldwide. People died so fast the local cemetery couldn't keep up with the burials and had stacked the coffins around the graveyard like dominos. When the rains came, the caskets made outstanding canoes and took off down the hill. In fact, the cemetery was running out of room altogether, but the coffins had to be fetched out of the river before disease spread faster and became even more deadly.

Okie officially took on the responsibility of caring for his mother and five brothers and sisters after his father died of consumption in 1923, and he took this responsibility seriously. Okie provided for them in every way and tried out a variety of occupations—farmer, lumberjack, and a gofer at the local dog tracks. He spent a short time as part of the iron crew on the American Insurance Union building, or Deshler Towers as it was known, in downtown Columbus.

One day while working near the top of the building, he watched a buddy fall and smash like a bug on the concrete below. Shaken and weak, Okie climbed down from his perch, walked out of the building, and didn't even come back for his paycheck. From that moment forward, Okie Rice would never again work for anyone else. He would call his own shots and do business his own way.

Over the years, he owned a pool hall, a bowling alley, a restaurant, a construction company, dozens of rental houses, and a used car lot. Okie was the first fire chief of West Jefferson, a small Ohio village located on the Old National Trail just a few miles upstream from Georgesville on the Little Darby. He built West Jeff's first in-ground swimming pool, too. But all those professions would pale in comparison to the vocations that made Okie the most money and the most famous—his gambling halls, the numbers racket, and his love of the Sport of Kings—horse racing.

He was, by any definition, a catch. Handsome, with a Clark Gable dimple and wavy brown hair, his dark complexion gave a healthy glow to a lean, economical body. Okie stood out among the gangster-style clothed men of the forties. When it came to fashion, Okie Rice was absolutely synonymous with class and style.

His suits were of fine linen, wool, or other natural fiber, either single or double-breasted but always perfectly tailored, with a crisply pressed cotton shirt, and impeccable tie. Sometimes he cocked a fedora just so above one brow and occasionally clenched a long stogie that peeked out beneath the brim. He had an eye for picking out just the right accessory to finish off his clothing statement—cuff links, a gold pocket watch, a vest, or a pair of suspenders was added to complement his outfit. This level of dress was considered daily wear for Okie, not simply for special occasions.

His inside breast suit pocket held a fat stack of cash unfolded and secured on each end by rubber bands. For Okie, cash was everything and the only currency of consequence in life. It was the defining icon of his self-image, providing a constant sense of comfort and security and a universal symbol of his notoriety.

Okie was proud to be a man's man and delighted to be a ladies' man, too. Sylvia Morgan was the first woman to catch him long enough to get married. They set up house in West Jefferson and began a family that would grow to four children—two sons and two daughters. The early years of their marriage were hectic times for Okie and Sylvia. Their gambling businesses grew rapidly, and by the early forties, Okie had made his first million dollars. Between the various businesses, staying one step ahead of the law, and raising a family, the couple needed reliable and trustworthy help.

They counted among their dear friends Loany and her husband Pete Dillon. Pete worked for Okie in his gambling hall, the Madison Club, and ran a numbers route for him, too. Pete was known for making a deliciously wicked cup of coffee, a skill Okie put to favorable use for himself and the patrons around the club. Meanwhile, Loany busied herself helping Sylvia run the house, working on the odds and ends befitting a millionaire gambler's wife. It wasn't long before Loany would add running a numbers route for Okie to her list of duties. The four of them easily blended friendship right along with the working dynamics of boss and employee, and they carried on together and had a grand old time.

Eventually, Loany and Okie began carrying on and having a grand old time of their very own, but it is likely that union did not start until after Pete was drafted into the Army. The one thing that is certain was Loany and Okie were not particularly discreet outside the eyes and earshot of their respective spouses. West Jefferson typified small and conservative farming communities in the forties— despite the presence of Okie's gambling hall—and this story was the biggest, the hottest, and the juiciest of gossip. People watched and whispered, speculating about the town's number one, most notorious celebrity.

According to Loany, it was Okie who began chasing after her and refused to leave her alone. Now, Loany was not Okie's first indiscretion while married to Sylvia, but she was the one to completely and utterly charm him. Flamboyant and edging on brassy at times, Loany was in character and style so distinctly unlike Okie's wife Sylvia who was more conservative, reserved, and proper.

Where the Lord Almighty skimped on height with Loany, he definitely made up for it in the cleavage department. At one or two inches above the five foot mark, she sported a DD set of assets that required special order brassieres to contain them.

As a child, my first request to help Loany into the special booby body armor was indeed quite a shock and a rather terrifying experience. Answering her holler out to me, I walked into the bedroom and found Loany standing half naked in the scariest looking get-up I'd ever seen. There had to be half a dozen sets of heavy-duty hooks running up the back and laces weaving their way up the front that covered a thick satin shroud as she huffed and puffed to try to get it to snap in place. I fumbled and pulled on the strange contraption, getting utterly nowhere.

"Come on, you have to be stronger than that," Loany laughed in encouragement. "You can do it!" I absolutely could not do it, and if this was what the bra thing was about I definitely did not want to grow up and out.

Dear God, may I please take after Mom's side of the family.

Had I ended up taking after Dad's side of the family, I could have shared in Loany's custom of rejecting a wallet to instead carry currency snuggly tucked down in between her lady lumps. Twenties, fifties, hundreds—much more cash than anyone should be carrying on them—often rested on board with her big girls. One day, she pulled several thousand dollars out of them at a real estate closing and nearly gave the title agent a coronary. I believe the potential heart attack, though, was from watching the extraction of the money take place. It was such an odd sight to the unsuspecting and uninitiated. Without warning and never missing a beat in any given conversation, Loany hooked the left thumb down into the cleavage center line to locate and loosen the stash while using her right hand to trap it, snap it, and unwrap it. Why write a check when anatomically equipped with an on-site bank vault?

And so went the antics of living and loving with Loany. She was full of boundless energy and fun, and every part of her daily tasks had the potential to erupt into an adventure. She adored people and spending time out and about socializing. Loany treasured clothes, makeup, jewelry, fine food, and fine things. She was fearless and committed to work hard alongside Okie and take risks as a fellow racketeer. Loany possessed superbly honed business street smarts and was one very attractive woman—a fine trophy for Okie in her own right. The significant detail of them each being married to someone else didn't seem to stall them one bit.

* * *

Kermit "Pete" Dillon had made it to Private First Class, which is the third rank from the bottom in the Army, but where many enlisted soldiers spend their entire time in the service. It also meant he had managed to stay alive one year and four months in the Sixth Armored Division of the Fifteenth Tank Battalion—the amount of time required to automatically be promoted to PFC. But, a few weeks after Easter in 1945, his luck ran out somewhere near Munich. The machine gunner in his tank was killed and Pete volunteered to take over, an offer not expected of a Private First Class. Shortly after he climbed into the gunner position, his life was gone, too. Some say he volunteered for the assignment because he had learned about Loany and Okie's affair, possibly by letter, or maybe he just knew by the barometer in his heart. Nevertheless, Pete's body was shipped home and came to rest in the Oak Grove cemetery on a hilltop overlooking the confluence of the Big and Little Darbys and the spot of land that would in time become Paradise Rice. Loany now added the label of widow to that of wife, daughter, sister, mother, and the other, notably less desirable nametags being thrown around to describe her, such as "floozy," "slut,, and "hussy."

Sylvia Rice would find out about Loany and Okie from a redhead's hot temper and desire for vengeance. The wife of one of Okie's horse racing partners and a woman not the least bit timid, she marched over to the house and unloaded on Sylvia. Unhappy about an aspect of her husband's business relationship with Okie, the redhead must have figured her line of attack would even the score with Okie but good. Although the news did earn Okie a divorce, it also left him free to marry Loany, or to continue to live in sin.

Loany and Okie lived a bit of both options. They would eventually marry, but not before living together for many years. They lived their unconventional and un-Christian lives right out in the open and ignored the talk and whispers of those around them. Loany simply did not care what others thought or said about her, period. She couldn't be bothered with such silly concerns, as life held more interesting and important matters to invest one's time in. Besides, right then Okie had a much bigger problem than the judgment of the local minions to concern him—a diagnosis of tuberculosis.

Okie had already beat tuberculosis once by finding a doctor who was willing to remove his diseased kidney, a practice not accepted at the time because a person just wasn't supposed to be able to survive with one kidney. One physician who would not perform the surgery was Charles Mayo, though Okie traveled to Minnesota in search of the best of the best.

"You have six months to live," Mayo declared solemnly. So Okie returned home in search of local, medical talent. Having access to the kind of cash required for such an operation certainly didn't hurt his chances. Okie later remarked you absolutely get what you pay for, because a friend of his in the same exact situation paid a doctor five hundred dollars to cut on him and died. Okie's operation, on the other hand, cost him five thousand dollars and he lived.

This time, though, the tuberculosis had attacked a lung, most likely migrating from the connector tube left attached to his remaining healthy kidney. The doctors in Ohio wanted him to go to a TB hospital and he agreed to take a look at it, but if the place wasn't satisfactory, he didn't ever want to hear about it again.

After visiting the center, he told the doctors, "You don't bring people here to cure them—you bring people here to die. Ain't no way."

Instead, he checked himself into White Cross Hospital, a Methodist facility in Columbus that was the beginning of today's mega medical conglomerate OhioHealth. Okie gave the doctor to perform the prescribed procedure one single order. Whatever the outcome, the surgeon had to finish the operation, even if Okie died on the table.

Okie survived the operation, but the nurses at White Cross wouldn't take care of him, because they were afraid of contracting TB. Not Loany. She stayed on watch continuously in Okie's hospital room and demanded he receive the proper care. When he stopped breathing one night, she called the doctor in to save his life. Loany was the one who nursed Okie after physicians collapsed his strong lung to build up the bad one, and then drilled a hole in his back to pump in air. She was the one who dressed the wound around that air hole. And somehow, Loany was the one who finagled it so Okie was permitted to convalesce at home in an upstairs bedroom, where he lived for one year, even though the laws required a TB patient be quarantined in a sanitarium. Loany fed Okie special concoctions of heavy cream and sugar. She continued to nurse him, unafraid to be with him. Between Loany's steely determination, Okie's money, and his luck of being able to take experimental drugs easily, three years later Okie Rice was proclaimed to be tuberculosis free, and he outlived Charles Mayo's prognosis by more than six decades.

Not surprisingly, Sylvia and Loany's friendship did not outlive the anger, hurt, and betrayal from the adultery committed by a onetime dear and close friend. Sylvia tolerated Loany when they both turned up at public events. But more often than not, Sylvia tended to remain in the background and eventually her presence faded away, overtaken by Loany's open ease, confidence, and command of the moment.

In 1952, Loany and Okie finally tied the knot in Indiana, alone on a road trip, most likely to attend a horse race. They would remain married "forever" and live long enough to see their golden anniversary. And, as they moved forward as husband and wife, life would just keep getting better and better at Paradise Rice.

CHAPTER 3

One Plus One Equals Twelve

"What was it like growing up? You mean spending Sundays with newspapers spread all over the dining room table counting money?"

—Perry Rice

The numbers racket operated essentially as the first lottery, before games like Mega Millions, Powerball, or Kickers had been conjured up. Playing the numbers was the simplest of betting games—a pick three with one digit tied to the stock market, one to futures, and one to local horse race results. A penny bet paid roughly five dollars, and typical wagers were a few cents, with a few dollars being a huge bet. It was possible in the forties and fifties to have a major presence in the numbers racket without any ties to organized crime. That was because ventures like these were privately financed by entrepreneurs like the

Rices who could manage the required cash flow demands, while possessing the balls of steel to romance, pay off, and dodge the law simultaneously.

Loany was born with a natural flair for business and a good head for figures. Being in the numbers racket with Okie fit her like the suits, coats, and dresses the Utah Milling Company traveled to Paradise Rice to measure and custom tailor for her. Teaming up with Okie gave Loany the means to manifest her innate sense of fashion and style in the very grandest of scale. The outfits she created oozed with utter elegance, from the opulent fibers she chose, to the bold and subtle colors she combined, all designed to accentuate her natural beauty, dips, and curves, of course.

While Okie possessed an entrepreneurial eye and vision, it was Loany who added the drive and organization necessary to steer the gambling businesses toward even greater prosperity and growth. She knew no other way beyond a life full of hard work, and she put her endless energy to use with passion and enthusiasm, delighted by the constant variety and adventure waiting in each day.

Loany often drove one of the countless numbers routes through big Ohio cities like Dayton and Columbus, or along sleepy country roads lined with fields of corn and beans into little towns like Xenia, Mechanicsburg, London, or Urbana. Two hundred miles out and two hundred back, she'd trek to pick up bettor slips and money. When word came the cops were hot and watching during the day, the numbers were run out at night. Slowly moving down a country gravel road, runners would blink their lights twice at approaching cars and then pull over to wait. If that car passed on by, they would repeat the routine for the next automobile until finally meeting up with the right guy.

One time along the way, Loany ran into a local deputy sheriff and threw the numbers slips she'd collected out of the car window and went back to dig the cache out of a ditch later. Sometimes she simply spent time visiting with the law or negotiating safe passage. How about a couple bucks, or perhaps something of value on board in the car? Jewelry for your wife?

For Okie, a palm derringer he carried caught a deputy's fancy. "What you got there?" the cop inquired. "Man, I've always wanted one of those," Deputy Dog added.

"Take it. It's yours," Okie offered, and that cop in Urbana never bothered them again.

Numbers were coming into Paradise Rice from three or four states, forwarded by those afraid to go it alone. In Ohio, there were runners and routes that formed a network and covered a sizable portion of the state. Some runners had amusing trade names like "Too Tall." Others were remembered for their creative antics to outwit the cops and deliver the goods, like Henry Hicks, whose trademark was a felt hat with a big wide band. One night after being picked up and hauled in to court, the judge asked Henry to remove his hat, and all the numbers slips spilled out onto the courtroom floor. Oops.

The Dayton police would put a reverse twist on a reverse twist, by taking half of runner Willie Willholt's "poke," the betting slips, and then turning him loose with all the money. He begged them to arrest him, to no avail, because not having the betting slips left Okie in a heck of a bind with his customers. *The Journal Herald* delivered up the Willholt story with soap opera drama and titillation, smirking along with the sting, but paying homage to Okie, too.

The numbers runners were a wide-ranging group, an extensive network of men and gutsy women from diverse racial, ethnic, and socioeconomic backgrounds. There were black and white, young and old, Italian, Greek, English, Latino, hillbilly, richbilly, Catholic, Protestant, and Jewish—whatever. That they came from most all walks in life hit close to home for me four decades later.

Visiting my home for the first time, Loany ooohed and aaahed at the transformation my family had accomplished through the magic of cleanup and renovation to the house I owned in the well-established midtown neighborhood of Westgate in an area of Columbus known as The Hilltop. Mine is a community of several hundred homes built before and after World War II, in a section of the city that produced mayors, doctors, lawyers, priests, and other professionals, along with solid working class families. First generation homeowners raised their kids there, took them to Westgate Park to play in the woods of majestic oaks, ash, and black walnut trees, to fish in the well-stocked pond, or to play a pickup game of softball, tennis or basketball. The residents most likely attended either St. Mary Magdalene or Parkview United Methodist Church on Sundays.

The annual Hilltop bean dinner was the social event of the year in Westgate, with a simple menu of soup beans cooked on open fires and served up with cornbread and coffee. Local businesses displayed their wares and handed out free samples. Bean Queens were chosen and a carnival stretched across the park grounds for the kids.

The event continues to thrive today, the modern version without the queen or the carnival. Cars line the streets adjacent to the park beginning around dawn, as this sacred day is also Yard Sale Saturday in Westgate. Early morning shoppers sift through blocks upon blocks of hidden treasures and junk, and make their way to the park to enjoy an antique car show, listen to live music, and shop the local vendors. Then, they wait in long lines to lap up homemade soup beans and cornbread, or feast on burgers, root beer floats, and other fair food.

The homes in Westgate were designed to be as unique and varied as the inhabitants, combining brick, stone, wood, and stucco into the styles emerging in popularity during the growth and prosperity of the early twentieth century. There were practical and adaptable Four Square houses with expansive covered front porches topped with a gambrel roof. A handful of Tudors and Queen Annes graced the neighborhood, their Palladian arched windows peeking out attic dormers. Stately Colonials spread out across two lots with their central entrances and columned canopies. Bungalows in every variation dotted the streets as did Craftsman-styled classics. There were Cape Cods and even more modern ranch style homes, too. These were solidly built dwellings with very little duplication in delivery.

I was so excited to have found my little Westgate treasure and that I was able to purchase it from the original owner before someone else got hold of it and attempted half-assed, screwed up improvements in the name of enhancing market value.

Loany fussed over and made a great deal of my modest pieces of furniture, strutted from room to room, and raved on about the plaster walls, hardwood floors, marble fireplace, and substantial half dome picture window that graced the living room. Meanwhile, Okie busied himself by checking out the pool table in the basement game room and gave it and the condition of the side rails his pool shark thumbs up. When I mentioned the vintage leather doctor's bag I found in the attic and marveled my house had been built by a physician, Okie piped up.

"Doctor? He wasn't a damn doctor. He ran numbers for me," Okie declared. "He used that bag to carry the slips. I think he worked for the railroad, but he worked for me, too," he went on to explain.

What? No doctor? I reeled between the thought of the cool attic discovery and this new revelation. *Darn it. I wanted my house to have been built by a doctor who left his first bag in the attic.*

My mind was jolted back to the present overcome with the sound of Loany's bellow of laughter. I listened as they reminisced, debated, and finally argued at length over who had lived where. Lots and lots and lots of people ran the numbers for Loany and Okie.

Beyond the movement of those runners, back at Paradise Rice there were phone bets for Loany to log along with helping Maxine enter the runners' slips properly into a ledger book. Payouts on winning bets were processed and prepared to deliver to the runners for distribution. Although Loany and Okie would easily come to cheat on each of their respective first spouses, when it came to betting and bookmaking their reputations for honesty and integrity were unparalleled and consummate. Neither could have rationalized not making good on a winning wager. Okie even returned a brand new 1949 Hudson convertible purchased as a graduation gift for his son Carol to quickly come up with the cash necessary to pay off a big bet. That five dollar wager paid out more money than a man would earn in an entire year from a decent paying job.

Every single day the stock market opened there was money to count—unfathomable amounts of cash to tally at times. Loany would later recall sitting one night at the kitchen table with the day's take of thirty-eight thousand dollars in cash piled in front of her. The silver coinage would make its ways to a bank the following morning, filling bags that each could barely be lifted by one man. The bills were counted and kept on-site to cover operations, living, and loaning.

Loany grabbed at the ones, fives, and tens. "One hundred for me," she'd say, sticking the bills into her cleavage, "and here's one hundred for Okie. Another for me. Another one for Okie."

Of course, none of Loany's fists of cash or cleavage stash was turned in to the Internal Revenue Service, and in all likelihood less than a third of Okie's money ever made it onto a federal tax return, either. Still, in one notable year, he paid forty thousand dollars in federal income taxes, which would be today's equivalent of roughly half a million dollars—and it would have been more like two million dollars had all the booty been accounted for.

The interesting paradox about gambling back then was that as far as the feds were concerned, it was perfectly legal as long as a person registered for a federal gambling stamp and paid the appropriate rite of passage to Uncle

Sam each year. Gambling remained against state and local laws, so to stay in the game, one had to contribute to a hefty list of "supporters." Cops, judges, sheriffs, and mayors around Central Ohio along with at least one governor all profited handsomely from payoffs and perks that found their waiting pockets.

Along with the straightforward conveyance of cold hard cash, there were simple gifts of charity like free chicken dinners for the patrons of the Madison Club every Wednesday evening. The birds were picked up fresh that day in London from a woman who fried and then packed them up in a huge wash tub so they could be sent back to the gambling hall to be served along with potato salad, baked beans, and the like. The law from the various local agencies would convene at the West Jefferson police station and then send word down they were ready for their dinner plates to be delivered.

The Madison County Sheriff is said to have ended up with a two hundred-acre farm Okie deeded in the lawman's name to hold and hide the asset. When he refused to give it back, what could one do? Turn him in to, say, the sheriff? Meanwhile, the Franklin County Sheriff routinely warned Loany and Okie of raids that were planned for Paradise Rice or one of the gambling halls. He left office and retired to a magnificent home in Florida, one valued well beyond the traditional pension buying power of a *shire-reeve,* all complements of Enterprise Rice.

During the war, one governor turned the heat up on the local Cadillac dealer after automobile production shut down. He demanded to know how some gambler took delivery of the last car available, a beauty the dealership's sales staff all knew he was most interested in, by the way. It was quite simple, really: the gambler knew more of the right people than the governor did, and spread his universal currency of influence deep and wide. Okie did end up returning the car to avoid downstream friction for himself or the dealership. Yet, he had mastered a marketing strategy of blending vertical and horizontal integration successfully, long before the terms turned up in a business textbook. And, Loany was the perfect partner to help implement both.

Young or old, rich or poor, a biker dude or soccer mom, one of Loany's secret weapons was her ability to connect with everyone by simply meeting people where they were. She made no judgments and took no prisoners; she merely got down to the serious business of living and loving in the moment. Loany was equally comfortable attending a poker game with Bob Hope and Bing Crosby over at John Galbreath's estate along the Big Darby on Kentucky Derby day, or sailing down the Florida coast in a yacht with other richy-rich, as she was sitting in a run-down diner, carrying on with the cook and waitress. She treated everybody the same and was unimpressed with wealth, title, or position. Loany could maneuver anywhere up, down, or across the food chain of gambling. She loved every moment spent with the people she met, and each one inevitably became a member of her growing herd of fans.

There were eyes and ears everywhere with plenty of volunteers thrilled to help the Rices out. They respected Okie, adored Loany, and wanted to be around both of them. It was easy to keep one step ahead of the law with all that popularity and admiration surrounding them. And, of course, there were the cash payoffs. As word continued to filter in concerning raid activity, the evidence was moved out of Paradise Rice and then back when the coast was clear. Bettor slips from earnings not turned into the IRS were stored in old lard cans in a hillside root cellar cave. After a couple months, the slips were burned to make room for a new batch to stash.

Indeed, the Rices made loads of money and spent loads of money; sometimes more than they took in, and sometimes less. They were multimillionaires during a time when to be so was truly a one in a million occurrence, an accomplishment of incredible distinction. Okie and Loany were ultra-rich before today's hip-hop-rapping, crib-flashing musicians or mega-endorsed sports figures existed in abundance and cable television familiarity. They belonged to a most exclusive club whose membership filled an "A" list of movie stars and business moguls whose addresses were not Georgesville, Ohio. Loany and Okie were the biggest of fishes in the dinkiest of mud puddles. The Rices were absolute standouts, and they were downright notorious.

Money was given away to most anyone who asked for it, and it was not unusual for a near-stranger to pull up at Paradise Rice to discuss a "loan" for a proposed business venture or debt. Detractors of gambling might have said the Rices' numbers racket was a sorry departure from Robin Hood's charge in that they took from poor people and then gave back to other poor people they knew or kind of knew. It was as true then as it is now that the bettors were often those who could least afford it. However, few if any of the local "poor" were turned down when it came to getting cash from the Rices.

Loany lavished gifts on family and friends—cars, clothes, cash, Cartier jewelry—from money tucked away creatively around the house. There was cash inside socks under the bed, in Loany's hat and shoe boxes, inside lamp shades, and behind a knotty pine wallboard in the basement. The one time Paradise Rice was robbed there wasn't much that could be done about it. How does one report missing illegal earnings, particularly when the theft was likely an inside job by one of the only people aware of the secret hiding places—the Madison County Sheriff?

Cash flow management was an essential component of Okie and Loany's business; having ready access to cash was critical to handling the ebb and flow of supply and demand. Without it business could not continue. So, after the robbery, a new "friends and family" security plan was swiftly and unceremoniously launched.

My father returned home from an errand one grey winter day. He had a paper sack in his hands—I did see that—but I didn't know what it contained. I heard my parents debating in hushed whispers. Random words became audible now and then, while others were garbled and unrecognizable.

A child's radar is often foolproof and infallible, as reliable as the blue screen of death when Microsoft Windows crashes. There are those moments when parents believe they are speaking in private, a vacuum if you will, all alone in their grown-up world. But, somewhere in the background may sit a child, listening and responding to their tone, their words, their body language, and their emotion. I didn't know exactly what *it* was they were arguing about, but I did know *it* was huge. And on that particular day, my mother's tone and words inexplicably told me as a five-year-old that she was upset, absolutely freaked out and very teed off, about whatever *it* was my father had brought home in that paper sack.

In a household where there was rarely any conflict, this single event became heightened and frozen in the memory. It stayed with me until I was well into adulthood, not immediately recalled, yet never quite forgotten, either. For, at that time, as a five-year-old, I didn't really care about the actual subject of the thing, rather, the tension and conflict *it* was causing in my world, my safety net of happiness.

"*Ron,*" my mother hissed as she opened the bag and looked inside. In response my father insisted *it* would go in the attic, for just a little while. No big deal. However, *it* was an incredibly big deal to my mom, as I saw and heard from my vantage point just out of sight in the kitchen, around the side of the refrigerator. Creeping toward the scene of the crime in the dining room to get a better ear and eye full, I darted in and out of sight, as I struggled to gather more information. My five-year-old's reconnaissance mission never did figure out what in the world *it* represented.

It turned out *it* was a sack of money, one hundred thousand dollars, to be exact, that the Rices had asked my father to hold. Two more identical sacks of one hundred thousand dollars had been placed with other relatives as well. Even today, one hundred thousand dollars is a big-ass amount of cash, and as a point of reference, at that time my father earned forty dollars a week at a nice paying job in the aerospace industry. Loany and Okie told him to just go ahead and stick the sack upstairs in the attic and forget about it. In a week or two they'd need it. And they did. My father delivered *it* and asked them to please never request such a favor of him again. Ever. And they didn't.

Yes, the numbers racket was indeed one full of favors, with helping hands of giving and taking stretched out in all directions and on both sides of the law. When horseman Shep Shepler stopped by one day to continue discussion with Okie about a joint business venture, he found a woman knelt down over a flower bed working away intently. She identified herself as the gardener and told him to go ahead and ring the doorbell. If someone heard it inside, they'd answer. A couple months later at the racetrack Okie motioned Shep over to introduce his wife.

"I thought you said you were the gardener," Shep stammered in embarrassment as he looked at the same woman now all cleaned up fine, attached to Okie's arm, and grinning up at him.

"Well hell, I am the gardener," Loany replied. "And I'm the cook, and I'm the maid, and the bookkeeper. Shit son, I'm everything."

In addition to all the other *everythings* Loany dabbled in, she also planned and hosted parties at Paradise Rice. In fair weather, these were grand outdoor and upscale events held most weekends and were open to all who happened to stop in, be they known or unknown. How she ever figured the headcount is a mystery. Still, no one was turned away or left Paradise Rice without consuming a feast well beyond a common man's means. Loany's process controls for managing and scheduling tasks along the critical party path were as predictable and repeatable as an ISO 9000 standard.

She took her management responsibility requirements most seriously; she had to personally touch and select everything having to do with the soirée. Loany would call an order in to Schuman's Meats early Saturday morning for one hundred or so T-bone steaks that were to be ready at a prescribed time. Meanwhile, she and Okie's daughter Marty would maneuver around town making shopping rounds to grab up the rest of the menu items from her preferred suppliers. The last stop was to swing by Schuman's and lasso the beef, then make it home in time to put in motion the preparation ritual and turn over the grill grub to the barbeque chef.

Guests came and went throughout the afternoon and evening. Parking was an absolute mess, with cars crammed sardine fashion onto the level areas of the lawn and tucked in around the stables. Revelers hiked in from afar and used the edges of the road as an overflow lot. When they finally reached the grounds of Paradise Rice proper, some guests water-skied up and down the Little Darby while others fished from the edge of the creek banks or off the island. Swimmers whooped and hollered as they jumped off the foot bridge leading to the island, or waited their turn to try the low-or high-diving board. Children took turns riding up and down the creek drive, guiding an elaborate eight-seat peddle-driven surrey Loany had mail ordered from

Paris, France. Music blared out porch windows for dancing on the tarmac, and there was always at least one poker game heating up in the basement party room.

And life at Paradise Rice ticked on in this fashion undisturbed.

CHAPTER 4

Sickletoy and
Other Games of Chance

*"I'd rather be around horses than some of
the people I've known in my life. I've never
given up on a horse I was working with...."*
—Richard "Shep" Shepler

L oany was either a most skilled bettor at the racetrack
or the luckiest of ducks when it came to wagering on
the Sport of Kings, thoroughbred racing. Opinions were
split on this topic. Some claimed her impressive winnings
had to be based on intense and detailed analysis of the
daily racing program, or maybe her good fortune came
from having access to insider information on the jockeys
riding that day and a particular trainer's strategy for a given
race. Others insisted her windfalls were simply a matter of
chance. Okie declared it was because she bet on every
horse in every race. But, that's why they call it Lady Luck,

right? Anyone can be a winner, any time, and anywhere. Why not Lady Loany?

One thing never in dispute was that Loany won big at the tracks. She certainly understood that to make money one often has to spend it, and Loany was not averse to churning through lots of dollars spread among a myriad of horses and races in an afternoon. She made straight bets for a single horse to win. She boxed bets and gambled on all probable combinations for multiple horses to win, place, or show. Loany parlayed winnings from one race to finance the next. But, whether by luck or wisdom or a bipolar combination of both, she usually managed to end a day ahead of where she started, thousands of dollars in the black at times.

When not wagering at Central Ohio's hometown thoroughbred racetrack, Beulah Park, she passed the time holding court and socializing with the familiar faces she met along her jaunt across the grounds. There would be scads of horse racing fans to discover there: in-laws, outlaws, and other relatives; childhood friends and recent acquaintances; and inevitably, those seeking to upgrade to first class designation with the Rices. All such were crammed along with ten thousand others into Beulah Park's Grandstand, clubhouse and betting parlors for Loany to bump into on race day.

Thoroughbred racing ruled supreme as the sporting choice for recreational pleasure, perhaps because there were limited competing distractions. It certainly had a huge following, and Loany moved effortlessly around this world of excitement. Whether seated in the grandstand, grabbing a bite at the Upper Clubhouse restaurant, or working her way through the paddock area to size up a horse, friends and family were usually in tow as she took in the chaos, hopes, and dashed dreams of the track.

Loany easily shared the winner's circle spotlight with the day's posse of closest friends and family whenever one of Okie's horses won a race. While she didn't make every event, the photo evidence suggests she didn't miss all that many, either.

Photographs captured a handful of wonderful and private moments when the world slowed down and included just Loany and Okie together, alone. Tanned and slightly smiling, their eyes were steady and certain, at peace, and content in the moment. In one image Okie stood offset behind Loany with a hand upon her waist. They were a matched set, a pair meant to be, in perfect harmony. Other pictures reveal frames packed full of people, some straining from a second row balancing atop tiptoes. These movie stars of the moment stretched and craned their necks around the back end of a horse or peeked between the stable boy's arm and reins of the winning steed to twist a face into the shot.

Okie would own twenty-seven horses over the years and post a banner year of forty-nine race wins. That's a lot of lipstick and photo ops for Loany. Okie's racing colors—the silks, jackets and caps worn by a jockey—started out as blue with white polka dots, then were changed to white with a red sash. Later, a chartreuse sash was added, right around the time the horses were put in his son Perry's name, to avoid a greedy fortune seeker's lawsuit. That move also better aligned Okie with the laws of the land, because it was illegal at the time for gamers with a registered federal gambling stamp to own racehorses. The Internal Revenue Service contacted Okie and asked who in the world P.L. Rice was, and, in typical fashion, he had his accountant very carefully and clearly explain the situation, later noting, "I don't mind the local police and the sheriffs and such, but I don't mess around with the federal government."

Okie's horses ran at all the grand tracks around Ohio and in the surrounding states: River Downs in Cincinnati, Beulah Park in Columbus, Thistle Downs in Cleveland, Waterford Park in West Virginia, and Wheeling Downs on an island in the middle of the Ohio River. His horses crisscrossed the United States towed in trailers or transported by air from Narragansett Park in Rhode Island and then on to the West Coast to Hollywood Park and Del Mar. The southern route included Oaklawn Park in Hot Springs, Arkansas and Sunshine Park in Tampa, Florida. During World War II when horse racing was banned, Okie set up shop in Mexico.

The Rices flew to the far away races in an Apache airplane they co-owned with friends.

Loany's role at the racetracks first was that of clandestine travel partner and secret lover, and she joined Okie when his schedule took him out of town. It would evolve in time to that of solo or duo horserace attendee, bettor, and Paradise Rice Ambassador. She busied herself at the races enjoying the people she met there, checking out the horses, and representing a stunning female specimen attached to Okie's arm. She was equally as spectacular when solo and could usually be found at the track even when Okie was too busy to join her.

The names of Okie's horses were as lively and colorful as Loany and the sport itself, suitable fodder for an adrenaline-packed Triple Crown event called by Tom Durkin, renowned sportscaster and public address announcer. *"The opening half-mile was the fastest in history. (voice rising)...Lil Abner and Colonel Wilson are blistering down the backstretch...and the pent-up power of Turbo Jet is rising.... Private Sam is getting busy on Ella Bella and they are surging as they move toward the top of the stretch...And (name drawn out) Cor-o-na-tion Boy has come away with the lead. Record time. Happy Guess and Stand Off are there...Shuffle and Bolder are dropping back...Nurse's Sigh and Noble Song, not today. Melmar's UN is under a heavy drive from the outside...Cosmos and Dawny are moving up and challenging the lead now too...they're neck to neck...and... here comes Hurry Blue who sweeps past them to the lead. He is pulling away by two, pulling away by three...Hurry Blue is ahead by four...Hurry Ba-lue has won the Paradise Rice Derby. Absolutely thrilling."*

There were a number of respectable runners in Okie's stable, and indeed a couple of impressive standouts. A horse named Welcome was a happy-go-lucky mudder, a former stakes horse with huge knees who loved to run on a wet track and only got better the deeper and sloppier the mud became. Welcome would win five races in nine days taking home a bigger purse each time, quite a showing for any horse's lifetime statistics.

Water Color was even more gifted than Welcome. But none in this eclectic collection of geldings, stallions, colts, and fillies would compare with Sickletoy.

Sickletoy was an absolutely beautiful black thoroughbred with a dramatic white star marking on his forehead. He came into the world with a God-given package of DNA that destined him a chance to declare a place alongside the great names of thoroughbred history such as Man of War, Citation, and Secretariat. Sickletoy was the son of Sickle, a respectable stakes horse bred by Lord Derby between Phalaris and Selene. Sickle was one of their first offspring to come from Great Britain to America and stand as stud. As a leading sire, Sickle's bloodline has spread throughout the world and has become the dominant male line in North America. The horse is responsible for founding the Native Dancer male line, which has one of the most powerful branches of the Phalaris sire line in North America. Sickle was a great-great-great-great-great-great grandfather of 2006 Kentucky Derby winner Barbaro.

To be sure, Sickletoy hit the ground with some darn good genes and impressive pedigree. He loved to run, had a competitive spirit, and was a joy to train and ride. He ran with horses that had beaten Assault, the 1946 US Triple Crown winner. He blew away the competition at Beulah Park in the Governor's Handicap, the biggest race in Ohio at that time. He playfully pranced and loped his way to victory as the hometown's pride and joy that day, such a cut above the rest of the field. Although the Governor's Handicap was indeed an honor to win, Sickletoy would go on to compete at the biggest parks in the US, in increasingly prestigious races, and with an all-star cast of thoroughbred competitors. He also would win in Mexico City and have the mayor pose beside him in the winner's circle. His talent earned him a spot in the Kentucky Derby lineup.

Okie's trainer wanted to show Sickletoy's stuff to people he knew in Hot Springs, so he took him to Oaklawn to run in the Arkansas Derby, a prestigious race considered a good practice event leading up to Derby Day. A few paces out of the gate, a filly stepped on Sickletoy's heels and cut him all up so badly he couldn't run in the Kentucky Derby. Okie was absolutely devastated for both himself and Sickletoy. His chance to add world-wide fame to his fortunes through the prestige that comes with the Kentucky Derby had been dashed in just a few seconds. Okie also was worried sleepless over Sickletoy, because he had dreamed of owning and racing thoroughbreds since he had been a poor boy in Kentucky. He cherished all his horses, but, like parents who hesitate to admit they have a favorite child, Sickletoy was unequivocally his.

The horse was now plagued with sesamoid problems, the most common ailment racehorses develop from their sheer speed and the overextension of the ligaments around the ankle joint, or fetlock. Undeterred, Okie would not give up on his Sickletoy. He hauled the horse to The Ohio State University and tapped into some of the best veterinarians in the country. Okie dumped a fortune into treatment and therapy to restore Sickletoy to his former glory. The horse was put out to pasture for a year to rest and heal, and then slowly built back up to regain his station among the kings and queens of the track.

Okie wasn't the only one in love with and rooting for Sickletoy. His magnificence and potential for greatness took the notice of wistful wannabe owners, too. One offered seventy-five thousand dollars just to have a race with Sickletoy. When Okie took him to Narragansett Park to open up the track for the summer meeting, another admirer followed him around all morning, badgering and hounding Okie to part with Sickletoy.

"I'll buy him right here on the spot, and we'll scratch him today," the buyer offered.

"No, no, he's not for sale," Okie insisted. "This horse is going to win today," he added.

Within moments of Okie's prediction, Sickletoy would step in a hole in the track and break his leg. This time, no amount of money or love could help him. Like Barbaro's fate many generations later, Sickletoy could not be saved and had to be euthanized.

Sickletoy's legacy would live on, though, through his progeny, Sickle's Image, named the Champion Mare in 1953. She was a tough little girl just like her daddy and managed the demands of being shipped coast-to-coast to run quite well. Okie watched her from afar, proud of Sickletoy's studly contribution to her lineage. Sickle's Image would win more than one-third of her seventy-three starts and live for years before joining Sickletoy in equine eternity.

* * *

The daily chores of feeding, grooming, training, housing, and moving all this equine flesh around the country required an extensive staff and a sizable supply of cash. Come race day, there were trainer commissions and jockey fees, stable boys and drivers to deal with, and the track fees to pay. There was the cost and care of the horses off track, too—the labor, land, and stables to properly board, feed, turn out, and exercise the horses, plus the veterinarian and farrier visits.

The strategies for training and running a horse were as many and varied as those involved in his keep. Some trainers liked to drill a horse, or work it a mile, to prepare to run three quarters of a mile. That way they knew the horse certainly wouldn't be short in a race. But that mile workout again and again could take a lot out of the animal, so other trainers preferred to work a horse to become fit, and then just race him. Once a horse was fit, the logic went, continuing to work him made no one any money and it represented unnecessary risk and injury to the animal.

When an owner or trainer decided to "give a horse a race," they weren't doing that to deceive the public; rather, they really weren't absolutely convinced the horse was fit enough to go the distance. So, they let him "run with company" to gain some experience. They would tell the jockey, "Rider, get what you can—but don't abuse the horse." There was no reason to push a horse getting beat five lengths at the one-eighth pole because he was not going to extend himself any further or better. Letting that horse "run with company" educated and motivated the thoroughbred as well as the other horses around him. Horses do pay attention to other horses, just like we humans do when approaching the finish line in a tight five kilometer race. Running against a stopwatch might motivate some, but not compared to the prospect of getting one's ass kicked right at the finish.

"Riding with a battery" was another sort of motivator to nudge a horse. The apparatus was a kind of battery-operated whoopee cushion for horses, controlled by the jockey to administer a minor electrical jolt, but one that did not hurt the animal in any way. Still, the "battery" was an illegal device to use, but in certain kinds of races, the gadget was considered standard equipment. They used to say if you came around the turn into the stretch and it didn't sound like a fleet of swarming bumblebees, someone wasn't carrying his load.

Okie had told his jockey to ride Happy Guess to win a particular race. The jockey had been drinking and stood out in the open at the track and announced, "Zzzzzzt, this son of a bitch is gonna run today!"

"Shut up, will ya," Okie cautioned, but he just kept on.

"I'll tell ya, Okie—zzzzt zzzzt zzzzzzzzt—this son of a bitch is gonna run today!"

When Happy Guess won that day, no one was the wiser about them running with a battery, and Okie earned the purse to dump back into his equine enterprise. Loany most likely bet on Happy Guess and won her wager to dump into her shopping and gift fund.

If the gambling hall profits from the Madison Club had subsidized the early days of the numbers racket, then the numbers racket helped fund Okie's love of thoroughbred racing. Although all three businesses existed through the years somewhat simultaneously, it was undoubtedly the numbers racket where Okie, and then Loany and Okie together, made the most moolah. That's not to say Okie didn't make some serious bucks racing horses, but his winnings probably were not more than he spent, in great part, because of unscrupulous employees and "partners."

Thoroughbred racing was a world where deals and double crosses could appear at the onset, absolutely identical, with a sleight of hand shift executed with little margin for reversal in real time. Keeping friends close and enemies closer was an essential and fundamental must, though not always foolproof insurance, either. And, either of those labels might switch on any given day.

Some stables used riders forty pounds or so heavier to slow the published practice times, thus potentially raising the odds and payoff when the considerably lighter jockey ran the horse to win. One-fifth of a second is the length of a horse, and in a sport where the fractional difference between infamy and obscurity can be as close as a nose, any edge is a good edge.

Some jockeys and trainers had their own deceptive agendas and betting strategies, driven by greed or arrogance. A jockey only could officially bet on his own mount, but other arrangements were easily made behind the scenes and off-track. A jockey might ride purposely not to win, or prevent a second rider from winning, thus allowing a third horse to do so.

It was anyone's guess what might happen when it came to the "Claims Game," where every horse in the race is for sale at a predetermined track price. The idea in a claims race is to keep the competitive field relatively equal, so a Secretariat doesn't show up at the local track to have a day of paid practice. A horse's "class" will most always beat the published "time" of one of a lower rank. No one has ever figured out why this is so, but it's a fact in pretty good standing. An owner who enters a horse in, say, a ten thousand dollar claims race better believe the horse is worth that amount to him, because anyone demonstrating the financial means who submits a claim slip prior to the start owns that horse, provided no one else is competing to claim it. He owns it the minute the gates pop open and whether the horse wins, loses, breaks a leg, or even dies during the race. A horse might run for years and never have a claim placed on him, or he might change owners as often as some women have plastic surgery.

Why a person would risk losing a horse he had invested money, love, and time in is unquestionably a mystery to the non-equine world whose pets are dogs and cats. Running the claim is an addictive rush that adds danger and sexiness to the equation and is an opportunity to scam the scammers. Say a horse had been buried altogether, purposely held back for a couple of years and then is bet on and run in a claim's race where the steed's odds were huge. If the horse wins that day and there is a claim against it, the owner will receive the claim price, his share of the race purse, and hit big and nearly break the bank from his long shot bet. In comparison, selling a horse outright seems ever so boring.

So, there were all sorts of potential strategies to reconnoiter in the Sport of Kings—those that were legal and those not so legal. Corruption in horse racing has been historically almost impossible for the ordinary fan to identify and even harder to prove. Sometimes it was beyond Okie's reach to manage when illegal tactics were operating right under his nose and coming from within the home team.

One trainer talked Okie into spending fifty thousand dollars to buy five horses at an auction in Kentucky, and then tried to cheat him out of the horses' ownership later. Another threw Okie's money around widely, wildly, and without discretion, admitting openly to his own champagne appetite while possessing a beer budget. Walking in a bar and ordering up rounds for the house, he'd then disappear for Okie to clean up the bill.

Then there were the jockeys who had their own ideas about things, too. Nurse's Sigh was slated to run in

Chicago and the jockey received instructions to "pull him," purposely not win, to save him for a later race. But, he ignored Okie's direction, placed money on Nurse's Sigh, ran him, and won. The jockey collected a huge payoff from the long shot odds.

Another jockey cheated Okie out of a horse in California named Shuffle. Okie had intended to pull him the first race and then run to win in his next event. The jockey had a brother who lived out there, and he put a claim in on Shuffle before the first race began. Of course, that meant he earned the purse when Shuffle won the second race. Okie was never, ever able to buy him back. A third jockey listened intently to Okie's instruction concerning a horse named Deb's Daughter, then lost his ability to understand and converse in English after he ran his own race his own way.

Of all Okie's business partners, Loany was most likely the only one who didn't take advantage of his generosity and trust. Being the love of Okie's life certainly gave her exclusive privileges the others didn't share, and their relationship would ripen into the complex and sometimes contradictory layers that come with half a century of living and loving together. She was Katharine to his Spencer, delivered up between them in packages that more resembled Clark and Marilyn.

Okie would go through life expecting and insisting Loany remain on call to be his personal chef. Bursting through the front door of Paradise Rice after a business meeting or a horse race he would bellow, "Loany, I'm hungry—fix me something for supper," before the door even banged shut. And the woman who commanded center stage would stop her life at that moment and cook him up liver and onions, or whatever his whim. Later in life that might mean she could be found hovering over the stove in her underwear and bra preparing breakfast at ten o'clock at night. Loany's devotion seemed so out of character in a post-Gloria Steinem world of women's liberation and gender equality. But, it suited the two of them and fit the mores of the times their union had been defined in.

Okie was adamant in joining Loany on her trips around town to socialize with friends and family during their twilight years. Try as she did, Loany couldn't get out of the house without him. Yet, Okie didn't possess Loany's social talents. Like an internal alarm, we observers set our watches. Fifteen minutes after their arrival somewhere, Okie would begin to fidget and mumble, then stand up and declare, "Come on, Loany. I'm ready to go."

To which she would reply, "Go on in there and sit down. I'm staying." And, for the remainder of the round this scene would play out repeatedly until Loany found someone to drive Okie home, or she would give up, and end up hauling him off herself.

As the years ticked by, there was one other scene that played out with regularity. Every night before retiring ahead of Loany, Okie slowly rose out of his white leather recliner, one hand against an arm for balance with the other clutching a cane for forward momentum. Once he stood upright, he rearranged his robe and glanced down to check on his slippers and the world around his feet. Then slowly, inch at a time, Okie maneuvered himself and his hardware next to Loany's chair, and strained his century-old body to bend down until he finally reached her. Shaking slightly, he gave Loany a goodnight peck on the cheek.

* * *

In addition to his loyal partner Loany, Okie had a posse of full-fledged supporters who were well oiled with cash of their own or favorably connected to work behind the scenes in the logistics and politics of gambling. One was a Catholic priest from a local parish who knew how to get things done with people, and he added his influence as collateral into the business mix. Okie used to say, "If that son of a bitch goes to heaven, then anyone can get there."

The priest, along with a drugstore mogul and a doctor, teamed up with Okie to start a second gambling hall on Columbus' west side. They invested money and worked together to fix the place up. One craps table came from an old springhouse owned by the priest and drugstore tycoon where the table lay sleeping, covered up with straw.

Another craps table was added to the mix since those gave the house the best return. The doctor had a roulette wheel sitting in his garage which they pulled into the joint, added more gaming equipment, and ran the place hassle-free for quite a while. Every time a raid was planned, they received a warning call. By the time the cops showed up, there was never anyone there to arrest.

There was one warning call, however, that would change Loany and Okie's life as they'd known it forever, and it came from a friend with the Federal Bureau of Investigations. One of Okie's bag men had been caught across state lines, and this was a transgression that could not be overlooked by the feds. Okie Rice was offered a forty-eight hour grace period to shut down the operations. In return he would remain a free man. While Okie had successfully negotiated a deal with the IRS and paid them a million dollars in back taxes in exchange for his freedom years before, this time the FBI proposed a very specific and quite one-sided deal. To avoid a long prison sentence in a federal penitentiary, Okie was to shut down everything. Immediately and permanently.

Okie made his last trip around Central Ohio to judges' chambers and police stations carrying twenty-five thousand dollars in cash with him to each stop.

"Boys," he proclaimed, "you're going to have to get your Christmas next year from somewhere else because I quit." Most didn't believe him.

But he was serious. The twenty-plus year gambling dynasty that had played out at Paradise Rice was abruptly and irrevocably over. Where Okie had been the initial architect and Lord Almighty to Loany's St. Pete, those roles were about to reverse.

CHAPTER 5

Jimmy the Parrot

"No more beer, Bob."

—Jimmy

It is not too terribly much of an exaggeration to imagine Loany taught many a sailor how to swear. Her sister Maxine never used a curse word until she started hanging around with Loany. I can say with great certainty having fifty years of substantial firsthand evidence that when it came to taking the Lord's name in vain, no one, and I do mean no one, equaled Loany's mastery of blasphemy. She had no prejudice between the Lord and his son Jesus—she called on either and both as the situation required. Ancillary concepts such as hell and damnation were often also included in the discussion.

"Well I'll be Gawt damned" for example, was a preferred phrase and mostly used to acknowledge a sense of wonder or surprise, such as when Loany requested an explanation to the inner workings of a marijuana water pipe. The ask came to a cousin and me during state fair time, a late summer Ohio event so akin to the very core of Loany's country roots and social drive. Her attendance vacillated between multiple day trips to nearly living on the grounds along with the transient carnies. Despite being held during the dog days of summer when breezes zeroed out, the humidity and temperature soared to sweat-soaking heights and the smell of garbage and animal dung progressively overtook the delicious aroma of elephant ears and smoking ribs, Loany just needed to be at the Ohio State Fair. If she wasn't, she might miss something.

On this particular Fair day, we were walking the grounds mindlessly shopping and people watching when Loany gravitated toward a hippy's head shop display. My cousin and I glanced at each other cautiously. Maybe she wouldn't find interest in or notice the paraphernalia spread out across a table. But a translucent purple bong caught Loany's eye, and she grabbed it up while turning back to us for enlightenment. I shot my most severe, *"You are older, so deal with this situation,"* glare at my cousin. I waited for the moment to pass, but Loany was prepared to wait longer, quietly looking back and forth between the two of us, clearly expecting an answer. A quick explanation was offered: "It's a pipe people could use to smoke marijuana." There, that should do it.

"So, how does it work?" Loany asked. *Crap.* Going any deeper into this discussion was certainly going to be incriminating. Squirming a bit before continuing, it was then pointed out that the bowl was used to hold the "tobacco." Hopefully, this would be enough information to satisfy her curiosity. What more would a seventy-year-old woman possibly care to know about a bong?

Lots more. Loany next pointed to the air hole near the bottom of the tube. "What's this for?" she asked. *Oh double crap.* All right then, let us just be done with it and move on. I joined in now, and we took turns describing various aspects of the mechanical properties of a bong— where the water went in the pipe, how to position one's mouth over the top. We pointed out how the hole at the bottom worked as a vacuum portal to help the smoke travel up the tube.

"Well, I'll be Gawt damned. Clever. Damn clever," Loany exclaimed, turning the pipe in her hands and holding it up as if using it. And then her eyes spotted some hidden jewel in the next booth, and she was off like a fart lost in a twister. End of discussion.

Why Loany favored any and all variations of taking the Lord's name in vain I never thought of asking. It was just her particular form of self-expression, an essential and fundamental part of the complete package known as Loany. While she thought nothing of ripping out a string of ear-shattering, Lord-based profanity, Loany did take incredible exception to the use of the F-word.

It was the night of the annual Halloween party my brother Bill and I threw together during our twenties, a raucous event that meant we could expect to spend the entire next day scrubbing my house from top to bottom. It wasn't that our guests were purposely careless or destructive, but putting a few dozen or so costume clad, beer-drinking and disco dancing revelers into my modest home always resulted in the need to strip and wax the hardwood floors afterwards, as well as to commence a complete fall cleaning regimen over the rest of the house. The party had brought us a bit of local notoriety; it was known in our circle as *The Party* to attend. We kept the decorations simple. Bill used a saber saw to proficiently carve a dozen or so pumpkins into jack-o'-lanterns; we had an MTV jack, clowns and traditional jacks along with a Fu Manchu jack, a Mr. Bill jack, and others scattered throughout the house. They rested on the mantle and bookshelves, in the bathroom, on top of the refrigerator, and most any open spot. A custom-crafted music tape blared nonstop from the stereo in the living room that had been transformed into a dance floor. A beer keg claimed the spot in the kitchen where a stove would have gone had I owned one at the time. A mix of work colleagues, friends, neighborhood locals and like-minded relatives, our core invite group, were always welcome to bring joiners along for the fun. So, it wasn't unusual to have no idea who the guests were, before or after removing their masks.

This year's party was turning out nicely. Among the Halloween attire we'd had gnomes, a samurai and geisha girl, Spock, a Spanish fly, Indiana Jones, nerds, Dracula, a witch, a ghost, and a drag queen. The beer keg was meeting demand and Todd's Pizza delivered fresh pies hourly, all orchestrated by owner and friend Bob. The doorbell rang, and I looked around to scan who had not yet arrived from the RSVP list. Two hobos were standing on the front porch looking in at us. As I opened the door a third figure pushed past the hobos, ran down the front hallway, and jumped into the kitchen poking a wooden spear around in the air. Laughter erupted as a guessing game began on who the person was behind the costume. The mask was that of a pigmy and incredibly exotic, complemented by a grass skirt, hoop earrings, and beads. Black sweater, leggings, and moon boots completed the presentation, and though an odd combination of costume articles, somehow in a way it worked. The popular vote was that the height matched a work colleague Anita, noticeably absent and expected to be in attendance. Someone called out, "Come on Anita, take off the f***ing mask. We f***ing know it's you," but the pigmy ignored the order and headed on into the dining room, jumping up and down and pushing the mask into the faces of the other masks. By the time the pigmy hit the living room, a line had formed and was in tow behind.

The two hobos remained outside the front door and refused my invite to join the party. I was becoming uneasy now; what if these people were here to rob us? I had read about those kinds of incidents, and why wouldn't any of them remove their masks? I grabbed my brother's arm and pulled him away from the pigmy show.

He rolled his eyes at my suggestion. "Look around here. Do you see how many big jock guys like me are here? I'm sure we can handle it."

"Not if they have a gun," I hissed back.

The pigmy was dancing now to the music for the crowd, *sans* spear, and clearly pleased at commanding center stage. A modest bit of the twist and loads more original gyrations, fists clenched and chest smacking, sometimes moving in time with the music, though mostly not. I turned back in time to see the grass skirt fall off and hit the floor. Snorts came from behind the mask, as the pigmy bent down, trying to locate it. And standing back up with the mask finally gone, my mind could not fit the face with the place and the moment. Most of the partiers were even more confused than me. A platinum-haired old lady in long underwear and moon boots stood smiling at us.

"For those of you who don't know her, this is my crazy Aunt Loany," I announced.

"Yes, yes, that's right. I'm Aunt Loany," she agreed while moving around the room to shake extended hands and talk with her new gaggle of adoring fans.

"Oh my God," the Spanish fly said, "that woman is so cool. Do you think she'll stay and party with us all night? I hope I'm that cool when I'm in my seventies," he added.

"No way she is in her seventies," Dracula said, leaning in to join our group talk.

Loany continued the meet and greet ritual, in no particular hurry to rejoin the hobo posse still waiting outside to transport her home. She addressed each person as if in a receiving line for the Pope, serious and wholly delighted to meet each and every one. She must learn everything about them before moving on. *How do you know Margie? Where do you work? Are you related to the Phillips boys out on Taylor Blair Road?*

Once satisfied the room had been worked adequately, she stepped back to address the entire cluster of goblins and ghouls. Loany raised her finger and swept it through the air, following along with her eyes as she surveyed the room.

"You kids and that Gawt damned F-word. Hell's bells!"

* * *

True to his moniker, Jimmy the parrot mimicked Loany's entire dirty word repertoire, a collection of obscene phrases in the English language with that special emphasis on religious-based profanity. The one notable exception, of course, was the F-word. Where Loany had the presence of mind to silence her acid tongue when children were around, Jimmy shared no such civility or restraint.

"Well, I'll be Gawt-daaaamned. Lee-ow-uh-ow-uh-ow-na. Daaaamned, Gawt-daaaamned," Jimmy squawked as he clawed around the interior of his prominently placed cage. The bird was a striking Amazon parrot Loany brought to Paradise Rice when he was twenty-five years old, after having spent his youth delighting shoppers at the local Red & White store. Loany just had to have Jimmy, and she cajoled the owner to part with him. His body was mostly green, and being of the short-winged variety of parrots, he stood a bit less than a foot tall. There were yellow markings on Jimmy's head and wings along with faint hints of orange and blue nestled in.

Amazon parrots are exceptionally smart, said to have the intelligence level of a three-year-old child. They are also social, loud, and chatty. Jimmy was all of these, with a potty mouth to boot, complements of Loany. He reigned supreme for fifty years at Paradise Rice as one of the most beloved pets among the other inhabitants of her on-site zoo.

There were the hundreds of ducks that nested along the creek banks down around the dam along with a few mean geese. Local motorists knew about their habit to migrate across the road toward the horse stables, but lo be the stranger who zoomed by and put a duck's life at risk or ended it. Loany would jump off the front porch, run into the road with fists raised yelling, "Slow down dammit. You stupid son-uv-a-bitch!"

In addition to the water fowl, a half-dozen peacocks roamed the grounds and shared their home in a pen at the bottom of the hillside with a couple of roosters and brood chickens. A diaper-clad monkey ate his meals at the kitchen table. Perry the prairie dog loved to chew on fingers and stayed in his crate on the front porch when guests were around, but Loany allowed him in the house from time to time to romp and play. There were various breeds and sizes of dogs roaming Paradise Rice over the years, including BeBe, a gnarly looking Chihuahua with one drooping eye, razor sharp teeth, and little time or patience for children. Milk saucers were placed out on the driveway for the stray neighborhood felines to lap on as long as they didn't bother the ducks. Horses came and went as temporary stable mates to White Socks the pacing pony. For a time, there was a goat that claimed the island in the middle of the Little Darby as his quarters.

But Jimmy the parrot was the only pet to live for such a length of time within the main domain of Paradise Rice. He would assume the title of guard parrot, screeching and loudly announcing approaching visitors. Jimmy also had an ear for traditional folk music.

"Cotton-eye Joe, Cotton-eye Joe, where you go, oh Cotton-Eye Joe."

Jimmy became a body piercer one Christmas Eve long before such accessories were in fashion. He jumped down off a wood window valence no one noticed he'd been perched on and joined the dining room full of dinner guests. Somewhere in the midst of the shrieks, arm flailing, and ensuing chaos, flesh met beak, and my mother won a pierced ear and a trip to the doctor for a tetanus shot. Jimmy was absolutely freaked out by the pandemonium. *Bad idea to join these people. Real bad idea.*

Jimmy was content to live sometimes in and sometimes out of his cage. He liked to perch on Loany's shoulder as she moved around Paradise Rice while she cooked. He sat on top of the refrigerator and watched her intently.

"Five, fa-five, five, five fa-fa-five," Jimmy chattered absently while pecking away at his sunflower seeds and mullet.

"Why, he can count," visitors proclaimed of his ramblings.

"Why yes, he can count," Loany would reply with a slow smile. And so it seemed. But what Jimmy really could do was parrot the numbers bets he overheard being retrieved from the kitchen phone and scribbled on scraps of paper for more respectable accounting later. Next to swearing and singing, documenting the comings and goings at Paradise Rice was a favorite pastime.

Jimmy spent warm sunny days out on the second story porch where he passed the time surveying the cars that crossed the Big and Little Darby bridges, or studying the ducks as they moved back and forth from the water's edge up onto the dam to fetch the corn Loany tossed from a wooden bin each afternoon. "Babies, babies," she yelled out announcing her arrival. The ground around her transformed from the beige tones of concrete to a sea of grey, brown, and tan feathers topped with shiny and bobbing green heads of the mallard males. Yellow broad bills rasping and quacking up at her, Loany sang back to them in a melody that was more talk and chant than quack or song. As the contents of each scoop hit the concrete, it exploded apart bouncing and tinkling down the slope of the dam, and small bands of mallards broke out of the flock, fighting and negotiating over individual kernels. Those that hit the water disappeared with a dabbler right behind them.

Jimmy might critique Loany's technique as she maneuvered a garden hose and nozzle around to blow off the mounds of duck poop deposited by all these water fowl living on-site at Paradise Rice. From the dam itself and the sidewalks that capped the porches to the driveway tarmac, Loany methodically commanded the water, by the slight flick of her wrist, to effortlessly send pebbles and poop shooting several feet and onto the grassy hillside. She never seemed to tire of the ritual, which was a good thing, given the pounds of poop a hundred or so mallards can, well, poop. From time to time she stopped, looked up at the porch and called out, "Jimmy. How's my pretty boy?" Jimmy chattered back, declaring his love and devotion to Loany.

The day Jimmy broke out of confinement and flew away, Loany was absolutely distraught. He remained gone for hours, and she was becoming extremely worried when finally, near day's end, the phone rang with news of his whereabouts. Jimmy had soared around three miles as the parrot flies into West Jefferson and was relaxing way up high in a tree. He most likely would have gone unnoticed indefinitely had he not been spewing a string of nonstop, colorful bad girl talk and other phrases with their origin undeniably linked back to Loany. When she arrived and raised her arm up to the sky and called his name, Jimmy plopped down ready to return home.

"Well I'll be Gawt-daaaamned. Lee-ow-uh-ow-uh-ow-na....Jimmy's a purty boy, a purty boy....purty boy. No more beer, Bob."

Bob was sister Maxine's husband, a lovable and naturally easy going, pleasant, and charming man. He had a twinkle in his eyes, coal dark hair, and an uncanny talent in his feet to perform all forms of dance with precision, artistry, and stylistic flair. He won Maxine's heart with his nonstop smile, love of life, and passion for dance. They were a perfect dancing couple and Georgesville's unofficial exhibition duo. Eyes locked and smiling, Bob and Maxine moved in precise harmony, effortlessly floating across the floor of the Community Hall to the Fox Trot, Waltz, or the Cha Cha. When they danced together they were perfectly aligned in spirit and happy at that moment.

As Jimmy the parrot accurately reported, more than dancing Bob happened to love beer. And whiskey. And most any other form of alcohol from which to imbibe. Occasionally his snockered meter climbed beyond the level of sound thinking, and rational thought gave way to the contemplation of feats of magnificent grandeur. The night his beer drinking perspective convinced him he could pull the tablecloth out from under a ten place dinner setting of dishes, Loany was not near as amused as my mother.

The event was the Georgesville Volunteer Fire Department's annual banquet, a celebration Loany and Okie attended, well, just because they were Loany and Okie. They weren't volunteer firefighters, but they were Georgesville's unofficial pope and patron saint. Besides, they wouldn't miss an opportunity to dress up, go out, and enjoy a free meal.

"Now hear this—sports fans," Bob spouted out to those within earshot as he stood weaving and bobbing above the table of banquet ware.

"Sit down and shut up, Bob," Loany demanded. "Dammit, Bob."

Bob would not be easily persuaded. "Ginny Bell," he called his pet name for my mother out to her. "Whadda ya think?"

"Oh, I think you can do it," my mother laughed, and replied back in encouragement. Others chimed in egging him on. "Go on Bob," and "Let her rip." Maxine's look was beyond embarrassment, to one of being absolutely and utterly mortified, not to mention wholly pissed off.

Guided by the fervor of the crowd's enthusiasm and alcohol's grand visionary properties, he found his magic moment. Bob squared himself against the edge of the table and took a deep breath. "Looky here," he proclaimed, as he grabbed the cloth and gave it a hearty tug. Those in attendance report that he almost made it, but the last couple of settings hooked up in the tablecloth.

"Jesus Christ Bob," Loany bellowed, to the sound of dishes crashing and exploding.

* * *

"Five, fa-five, five, five fa-fa-five. Well I'll be Gawt-daaaamned. Jimmy's a purty boy. Purty boy. Dammit. Lee-ow-uh-ow-uh-ow-na.... Lee-ow-uh-ow-uh-ow-na.... No more beer, Bob."

CHAPTER 6

Murder in Paradise?

"If his wife dies in less than a year, then we'll know he did it."

—New Year's Day, 1963

Twenty-five years would pass after Loany's son Jerry died before she ever put up her signature Christmas tree again. And true to form, her distinctive holiday tree was indeed as unique and memorable as its creator. It wasn't some traditional pine or fir decked out in blue bows or parrots to set it apart, though come to think of it, parrots would have been a great theme for Loany. It was a small sapling Loany found along the Little Darby as she walked the bottoms searching for just the right one to transform into her special form of magnificence. She preferred to not sacrifice a hardwood like an oak or maple. Loany searched for a softwood scrub jammed into a growth where cutting it out would give the others a better chance for majesty. Height was not nearly as important as the number and placement of the branches. The ideal sapling would have six or seven substantial limbs with some irregularity and interest, but not too one-sided to be unstable and risk tipping over.

After topping and trimming it to fit indoors, Loany strung colored lights up and down the length of the branches to define them and then began the laborious process of wrapping each limb and trunk with cotton strips to cover the light cords and simulate fresh fallen snow. Shiny, chrome double-indent bulbs, delicate hand blown glass teardrop ornaments, and silver tinsel dangled from the branches as if angels had suspended them in air. The glowing lights traced the branches outlined in snow, and there were stars, angels, bells, musical instruments, and wooden horses gently rocking alongside Santa figurines and reindeer. It was the most beautiful thing I'd ever seen.

A few days after Jerry was laid to rest, Loany hurled the tree bulbs and all off the balcony porch where it toppled and crashed down the hillside. It was an act of rage and it was an act of helplessness and utter despair—the culmination of her unbridled desperation, remorse, and sorrow for not having been able to save him, her sweet son, "Butsy."

Jerry, who answered more often to his childhood nickname earned from running round and round while butting the air like a ram, was gone. Loany would never see her Butsy boy lope into Paradise Rice again, his lazy and good-natured smile lighting up the room. She would not feel his constant five o'clock shadow rough up against her neck as he squeezed her from behind in a bear hug.

Butsy was all that was left of Pete. And now he was dead at thirty years of age. Butsy's demise was so unlike any of the rest that had been taken from her—Margaret, Ruth, Wesley, and Pete. Those other deaths had come naturally, by fate, happenstance, or bad luck.

Why had it taken her so long to see what so many others saw? Standing on the porch, the cold winter wind trapped tears against her face, and the pain of the despicable truth ached deep from within her. Loany's comfortable accounting of life's certainties was irreversibly shattered, like the moment one awakens from a dream, and the lazy nether world of the night dissolves quickly from conscious grip as the reality of the here and now crashes into sharp focus. The moment of that shocking enlightenment about the horrendous thing that had happened forever altered everything for Loany, and she was stuck living with the heinous truth. It was Loany's first sickening thought awakening in the morning and the same one that robbed her sleep at night. Butsy was dead. Butsy shouldn't be dead. And that son of a bitch did it.

* * *

Doc was one of a handful of physicians practicing in the area during the sixties. He had attended The Ohio State University, played on the football team there during his college years, and was part of legendary Buckeye coach Woody Hayes' in-crowd. Doc loved everything sports and was incredibly active in Ohio amateur athletics at both the high school and college level. He was a pillar of the community, belonged to many sporting organizations, and sat on various committees and boards. Doc received a distinguished service award for his work, and a highly coveted scholarship would later be named for him.

He set up shop in earnest and strived to become one of the area's most prolific supporters. Doc worked with the high school booster club, county hospitals, and an educational economic development fund. He was a member of the local Masonic Lodge and also did good works for the Shriners. I guess you could say Doc was locally famous.

One would not describe Doc as a looker, and most certainly not as a sharp dresser. His appearance was invariably sloppy; wrinkled shirt half unchecked and hanging out over his paunchy belly and straining belt. Doc's critics would say he was also not remotely charismatic. But boy, did he have a flock of the faithful in West Jefferson. Stories circulated about Doc driving a tractor down impassable snow-covered farm roads with physician's bag at his side. He continued to make house calls when the rest of the world gave up the notion. Doc forgot to bill struggling patients and quietly paid tuition for a number of those who, without his assistance, most certainly would not have attended college. He was on call any time, every day and used to say, "You can't abandon sick people just because it's a holiday." His wife, a nurse, was always steadfastly by his side.

Doc's fan club hailed him as a near god. There were legendary accounts of his amazing feats and command of medicine whereby he had brought numerous patients back from the brink of death. His healed admirers teared up when talking about him and vehemently defended Doc and his cause. They had to, because he also had a large crowd of detractors, who responded to the tales with, "Probably wasn't even sick." It seemed people either loved Doc or loathed him. At his funeral Woody Hayes would deliver the eulogy, and a columnist at the local paper waxed poetic about the loss of a great physician, a "beacon in a storm."

His business flourished, and Doc eventually hired Butsy's wife Norma to help out around his office. Not that Loany hadn't always lavished over Butsy and his family in her own way. She spoiled him silly while a child living at Paradise Rice and then continued the ritual of excessive giving after Butsy was a grown man. His family didn't want for anything; not cars, clothes, cash, jewelry, trips, toys, accessories, or sundries. Butsy was embarrassed at times about how Loany carried on over him. He felt bad when Okie's daughter Marty didn't get the attention he did while they resided as step sibs at Paradise Rice. Butsy would call

Marty aside and give her gifts and small trinkets to try to make up for Loany's lopsided commotion and appearance of blood kin favoritism.

Butsy was a kind and gentle soul, content to work and live a simple life and ordinary existence punching in and out every day as a janitor at the General Motors plant. He took life as it came and did not seem driven with Loany's ambition and determination. The extra bucks Norma earned working for Doc came in handy during those days, because by the early sixties Enterprise Rice was trending downward. There was still some money, sure, but not the colossal amounts of days gone by.

Doc was quite taken by Norma, an energetic, friendly, and happy woman who, like him, was driven by a kindness and desire to help others. Doc was so impressed with her; in fact, he began to show up around town at places and events Norma attended. When he stood all evening by a booth she was working at the Georgesville Fish Fry, others began to take notice, too. No one could remember seeing Doc at the Fish Fry. Ever.

Doc wasn't concerned about requesting personal errands of Norma, either. Should his whim of the moment be some trail bologna from Loany's country store, he was not the least bit shy about interrupting the Goldhardt family Sunday dinner with a phone call to make his demand known. Eventually, Doc's perpetual presence had begun to annoy Butsy.

"It's the middle of Sunday dinner, for God's sake," Butsy snapped. "He can just wait."

More words were exchanged between husband and wife while members of the clan sat by quietly, pretending to be invisible. But Doc was a hard man to say no to, and invariably Norma left dinner, fetched the bologna, and delivered it up.

Of course, it wasn't long before rumors began to circulate about Doc and Norma. Good Lord. What was going on here? Nosy neighbors reported seeing Doc's car at the house regularly while Butsy was at work. Norma herself sensed others were suspicious and pulled family and friends aside to assure them nothing inappropriate was going on. But Doc continued on doing and saying as he pleased, unconcerned by appearances and idle gossip. Little by little, Norma was becoming a more important figure in his business and philanthropic undertakings. And just as the townspeople had whispered two decades before about Loany and Okie, now West Jefferson's most infamous pair to speculate about was Doc and Norma.

Loany was a member in good standing in Doc's fan club early on. She admired him and considered him a fine doctor. Damn good doctor. She thought nothing of Butsy seeking Doc's expertise when sick with some bug he couldn't seem to shake. It was a most obvious and excellent choice, particularly with Norma working close by. The diagnosis was that of amebic dysentery, most likely picked up from some bad drinking water while Butsy and Norma were on a vacation in Tennessee. A save-the-marriage trip, according to insiders, as the *Enquirer* would say.

The dysentery lingered on and on; Butsy couldn't shake it no matter what Doc prescribed. Weeks passed, and he was still sick and getting sicker. The fever, chills, constant diarrhea, and vomiting all left Butsy weak, dehydrated, and listless. He attended the Georgesville Fish Fry that summer wearing pajamas and slippers, and the short walk from his modest home adjacent to the fire hall took all the strength he could muster. Somehow Butsy made it down the back porch steps and the fifty odd paces across the yard and sat on a ledge next to the fire house beside the command central awning. This was an ideal spot for him to see most every attendee at some point. When my aunt strolled by his base camp, Butsy looked up at her and said point blank, "Betty, I'll be dead by Christmas." My aunt quickly moved away to shelter us kids from the conversation.

"Now, Butsy," she replied, "I'm sure you'll get better." Though, neither she nor other family members were all too sure.

My aunt may have shielded my ears from the mature-themed adult talk, but she was not able to quiet my six-year-old mind from the thoughts and fears that crept in whenever I was around Butsy. Why did he look so tired? Butsy had a sour and sad look on his face all the time. His skin had an icky color and was so pale I could almost see into him. Why didn't Butsy laugh and play anymore? Would my mom and dad get sick too? And why did all the grownups whisper and talk in low tones whenever his name was mentioned?

The man whose birthday was side by side with mine on the November calendar now scared me. His presence was a stark departure from the one I remembered at the cake and ice cream parties we shared with Norma and their daughter Pam, all gathered at the Formica table in the black and white checked linoleum kitchen. There were party hats and horns, balloons, and pretty flowered cakes with candles, and my name written in script icing. Butsy laughed and fussed over me, and we sang happy birthday and blew out our candles together. I couldn't imagine celebrating a birthday party with him this year.

As the summer of 1963 closed, Butsy was still fighting the dysentery and losing. Loany hovered by in the near background, her position of mother outranked by those of wife and doctor. The influence she might have wielded from the power that accompanies money was gone. She watched helplessly as Butsy was admitted to the hospital, once, twice, then again and again. Loany was beginning to silently question Doc. Nevertheless, as much as her doubts surfaced, her faith that he possessed extraordinary skill quieted those moments of uncertainty. Most of the time, anyway.

Butsy, on the other hand, was not so taken with Doc. He accused Norma outright of having an affair with the physician and not wanting him to get well, which was pretty much how a number of friends and family saw it, too. Nosy neighbors chattered on these two subjects with increasing regularity, having gained access to the details of the family's lives from the necessity of needing to lend a helping hand. Butsy's health had failed to the point he could not walk without assistance.

Death by dysentery would have been a slow and horribly painful demise for Butsy. As the months dragged on, he wasted away while enduring dreadful agony. Blood transfusions provided him no relief. By Christmas Eve he lay on a couch in the back sitting room at Paradise Rice, jaundiced, weak, his skin so translucent on areas of his exposed arms it appeared blood was seeping right through it. Most everyone knew Butsy was going to die soon. He pulled Marty down next to him and told her he loved her. She couldn't answer him back. She wanted to say something to comfort him and to tell him how much she cared about him, but her throat and tongue swelled thick as her mind raced to find words that would not come. It was the last time most any of us saw what was left of him in life again.

Butsy missed his Christmas death prophecy by three days. This time Doc decided they couldn't wait for the squad to come with medics to resuscitate him. Butsy was loaded into the back of the physician's station wagon, and he died in the car on the way to the hospital.

The mood at the funeral on New Year's Day went far beyond the imaginable for an intimate group of Loany's family and close friends. They sat together trying to hide their anger and regret for not having done something, anything to stop this insanity. Stunned by the terrible thing they had all witnessed unfold in slow motion, unable to do anything about it, they reviewed the opportunities lost. What should they have done? And just who would they have shared their suspicions with? The authorities? Who would have believed them? Doc was a God figure. They were perfectly aligned in their thinking on the topic. "If his wife dies in less than a year, then we'll know he did it," one said with steady conviction.

***

Doc's wife died sixty-eight days after Butsy at the age of forty-three. It was sudden and it was entirely unexpected, even to those who had dared utter aloud their suspicions at Butsy's funeral. No one could recall having heard she was sick. She seemed all right whenever anyone ran into her out and about West Jefferson.

That physicians have long been discouraged from providing their family members' medical care didn't put off Doc one bit. Nor did the fact that Columbus, Ohio, was not some remote island or the scene of a desert hiking accident at the bottom of the Grand Canyon where medical care was unavailable. Doc threw the nurse assigned out of the room, and he and Norma personally saw to his wife's care, medication, and shots. The nurses and other hospital staff whispered about the goings on in the room. This Norma lady wasn't a nurse. What were they doing? And where was this woman's, uh, official doctor?

This time someone did speak up, at least as much as a member of the medical community dared condemn one in the fold of its sacred fraternity that existed back in those days. Doc Henry, a colleague at the hospital, was so upset by the events he witnessed and heard about that he confronted Doc outside the hospital room shortly after his wife died. Doc Henry grabbed him by the collar and shook him hard. "I want you to leave this hospital," the physician snapped, as he pinned Doc up against the hallway wall.

"That son of a bitch," Doc Henry later told Loany when she approached him to talk about her doubts surrounding Butsy's death. The physician's anger, passion, and unwavering testimony brought legitimacy, an unbiased and definitive confirmation that sealed the deal for Loany and family members.

When Doc and Norma's families left together on a trip two weeks after his wife's funeral, it sealed the deal for West Jefferson's gossip meter, too. It rocked off the charts. After the couple returned, they stopped in at Paradise Rice unannounced, to clear the air. They wanted Loany to understand and to put her mind at ease about the awful things people were saying. This was not a remotely good visit, and the conversation was anything but friendly. When the exchange escalated to loud and ugly, Okie's son Perry stood up, unfolded his lanky basketball frame and towered over the group. "You need to leave now," he commanded in one simple statement.

That moment marked the end of Loany's relationship and access for many years to her only grandchild, Pam. The fallout and divide was complete and final, and Loany got a little crazy after that. It was the kind of crazy only parents who have buried a child can really understand. It was the kind of sorrow and desperation that goes along with the loss and separation of the direct and concrete living link to a body and soul.

The hurt of each parting was equally unbearable, yet in different ways. The pain of Butsy's death was agonizing in its finality and irreversibility, but Pam's existence—alive as she was and just out of reach—was utterly maddening to Loany. She had to mourn the death of a girl who was not dead. She longed for their times together—the walks they shared down to the dam to feed the ducks, and the road trips to Florida, where Loany paid a quarter every time she cursed, then invariably had to borrow money back from her granddaughter to pay at the toll booth.

There was no substitution for the flesh and blood bond of a son and a granddaughter, and there was no getting over any of it for Loany. For the first time in her life, she was incredibly hard to deal with or even be around at all. Her dancing eyes and ready smile were replaced with an unfriendly glare accentuated by deep crevices that outlined her face when she spoke. Loany was cranky and quick-tempered. She snapped and argued over any little thing. Loany and Okie bickered constantly, their marriage tested and strained to the brink of collapse.

During dinner at her friend Nadine's pizza place one evening, the woman pulled Marty aside in a bathroom to have a word in private.

"She's treating Okie terrible," Nadine said. "You need to do something about it."

"Hey," Marty was quick to reply. "Leona took care of Daddy when he was sick. Now it's his turn to take care of her."

No one could comfort or take care of Loany. Her despair and resentment deepened, fueled on in part by the others who shared their reservations over the two deaths. Among those were a local nurse and a second doctor from the hospital, an anesthesiologist who lived a few miles down the road from Paradise Rice. Their words both cut and cleansed Loany. She was perpetually stuck in the moment of the horror that culminated at Christmastime in 1963, but the testimony of those who knew the truth heartened Loany and quieted her mind, too.

Despite all the questions and uncertainties about the death of Butsy and Doc's wife, no investigations were ever conducted. Nor were coroner autopsies requested, because this was Doc we were talking about, after all. The words on their death certificates remain unchanged and unchallenged, both filled out by Doc, though his wife's was signed by another physician. These were certainly different times. That final testimony for Butsy proclaimed his death was caused by a massive gastric hemorrhage due to hepatic insufficiency, or liver failure. The death certificate of Doc's wife stated she suffered multiple pulmonary infarcts due to thrombophlebitis in the right leg, or a blood clot gone awry.

Maybe. Maybe not.

* * *

Kenneth Ogilvie ended his work day like most every other. He punched out at General Motors Fisher Body plant and roamed the parking lot in search of his car among the thousands of others there. Kenneth drove six miles to West Jefferson where he was staying with son David and daughter-in-law Lucille. Entering the kitchen, he spied chicken sitting out on the counter thawing for the evening's dinner. What Kenneth didn't see or hear was any sign of Lucille, a tall, striking woman with coal black hair. But the chicken was evidence Lucille was already home from her job working as a nurse for Doc.

Lucille had harbored suspicions about the death of Doc's wife over the years, but she managed to quiet the nagging thoughts and separate her doubts about it from her daily nursing duties working for Doc. She tended to the sick and injured patients, but privately shared her views with at least one person, Loany.

For the past couple of weeks, Kenneth noticed Lucille had been acting a bit odd, in fact, downright strange at times. And he wasn't the only one to comment on Lucille's departure from efficient nurse, homemaker, and gracious hostess. Lately, she was withdrawn and somber, almost zombie-like. The week before, Lucille rose up abruptly from the couch in the middle of a conversation, walked past the group of guests as if she didn't even see them, and disappeared into her bedroom.

On this particular evening, with Lucille nowhere in sight, Kenneth thought she was probably as tired as he after a day of hard work. He entered his bedroom, shut the door, and laid down to rest until dinner.

When David Ogilvie came home two hours later, he found his wife lying dead on the floor. Lucille's death certificate ruled her end a suicide from an overdose of chloral hydrate. She was forty-seven years old. The Madison County Coroner didn't conduct an autopsy.

* * *

Loany spotted me first and stepped out from behind the meat counter at Goldhardt's Grocery. She walked toward me holding a substantial butcher knife.

"How's Patrick?" she asked, unaware of the knife that bounced in the air accentuating each word. "Your dad told me he talked to him."

Loany absolutely adored Pat, my high school sweetheart, and lit up whenever we stopped by Paradise Rice to visit. Pat was a wonderful first beau, a friendly and easy going person who fit in effortlessly with my immediate family and extended Goldhardt relations tribe. He always received a classic Loany welcome—a slap on the arm, poke in the side, or gentle hip bump to knock one off step, as she bellowed a boisterous hello.

Loany wasn't the only one concerned about Pat. We were all worried since his mother had died quite unexpectedly from a cerebral hemorrhage two weeks before. Pat's stepfather seemed to be hurrying things along at nano speed with respect to the estate paperwork, with the help of a nephew attorney who owned a fancy home down on the Ohio River in Marietta. I'd spent a confusing afternoon there along with Pat's closest friends after his mother was buried in the country church cemetery where her father had been a preacher. The disturbing part of the wake was it more resembled a legal hearing to us out-of-towners than a time of comfort and fellowship. We met in the back hallway of the house and compared notes in whispers; something just didn't seem right, at least about the timing of things.

"I've talked to him. Kevin's talked to him," I replied in answer to Loany's question. I followed her as she moved back behind the meat counter. "We've all told Pat to slow down and take his time. Things don't have to be settled in three or four days," I continued. "He just wants it to be over with," I added, trailing off.

"I don't want him to have regrets," Loany said. She was still holding the big butcher knife and waved it in the air dramatically. "I so regret not looking into Butsy's death," she said slowly, shaking her head with a look of faraway sadness.

What did his death have to do with this? There was nothing suspicious about this woman's death. I couldn't believe Loany was talking to me about Butsy. She had never uttered a single word to me on the topic in the dozen years that had passed, and I had so many questions. "Well, what do you mean?" was all I managed to ask.

"The nurse," she exclaimed, as if I should already understand her cryptic comment, obviously forgetting I was seven years old back when Butsy died. "She tried to tell me," Loany continued, raising her voice. "She said, 'I have something to tell you,' and he walked in and said, 'Oh no you don't,' and led her out of the room."

The nurse? Where? What room? I stood looking at her blankly, trying to sort out her words in my mind.

"He gave her a shot, you know," Loany revealed, talking faster with disgust in her voice as she spit out the words.

Gave who a shot? The nurse? Which nurse? Shit. I am totally lost, I thought to myself. "Who?" I asked, with an unimpressive one word question.

"Doc, dammit! I'm talking about Doc." Loany paced back and forth, noticeably agitated, and she moved next to me like the closeness would connect our minds into a harmony of comprehension and enlightenment.

"Margie Anne, you have to make Pat understand," Loany beseeched me now. "You have to make him see. The decisions he makes now are final. He can't go back." Tears filled the bottom of her eyelids as she spoke.

"Loany, put the knife down," I said, more a request than an order. She seemed annoyed with me and then confused. Looking down at her side and the knife, Loany burst into laughter.

"Jesus Christ," she blurted out, amused at my jumpiness. And that was that. The spell was broken. Loany returned to carving meat off the bone to grind up and turn into ham salad.

"Here, what does this need?" she asked, jamming a spoonful of the first batch into my face. Loany had said all she cared to and never broke her silence with me again about Butsy's death. And I never found the right moment or reason to bring it up on my own. Loany had talked quite frankly with other family and friends over the years, but it just didn't seem to be my right, even now as a young adult. My station on the topic was eternally defined as the kid I had been in 1963.

As the years continued to stack up, some things softened in their own way and time. Loany's granddaughter slowly reappeared in her life. Pam's presence back at family gatherings was as strange and unsettling to me as her initial absence. One day Pam simply had been gone. There were no more play dates and slumber parties where we built blanket tents in the wide hallway that divided the living room from back bedrooms and bath at Pam's house. She was not there to hold my hand in protection or give me a stuffed toy monkey when I was frightened by the dark. But suddenly my older cousin was back, familiar, yet unfamiliar, and over time the repetition of her presence overwrote the years of sadness and separation.

Then, one holiday season I walked into Paradise Rice and it was back too—Loany's magic tree, positioned graciously between the dining room and back sitting area. It had been so long since I'd see one of her creations, and it was even more beautiful than I remembered.

"You put up your tree," I exclaimed in delight, as I hurried back toward the kitchen to find Loany.

"No," she answered in correction. "Maxine, Ruth, Norma and Pam put it up," she continued matter of fact.

Her words hung in the air—I was absolutely stunned. I never expected Loany to welcome Norma in her home ever again. But a sister on both sides of the divide had built the proverbial bridge and smoothed the road on each end of it. By taking the liberty to force the reunion, they marched into Loany's life like it was standard operating procedure.

I stood in the kitchen breathlessly waiting for what Loany would say next. She offered no editorial comment either way. Loany didn't gush with excitement and enthusiasm, nor did she roll her eyes and spit insults. Loany laid out the present state of her universe with the voice of steady acceptance, simply living in the here and now, though the ache of the past lay just below the surface.

CHAPTER 7

Goldhardt's Grocery

"Where in the hell is Leona?"
—Maxine Geddes

With Butsy gone and the gambling businesses closed down by the feds, Loany began to spend more and more time up the road at Goldhardt's Grocery. A logical next occupation for her, it was the kind of choice people of her generation made straightforward and matter of fact. Loany didn't strategize her career in the way someone would do now in a globalized world market. I could never imagine her thinking, *Hmmm. If I do the transfer in Chicago for maybe a couple years, I can parlay that into a European assignment and then return back to corporate and snag a vice presidency for sure. But, should the markets go all to hell in Europe, I could take over for Thompson in Asia and then be back in New York, say, in five years tops.*

No. And hell no. Her parents, Ollie and Gwenzora, had scraped out a living from the original one-room country store after Ollie found out the little honky-tonk gas station and the house beside it were for sale in Georgesville. He moved his family down the road a few miles from their homestead next to the Billy Goat Gruff railroad bridge and transformed the shanty into a mercantile business.

By the early sixties, the store had grown from its original one-room wooden structure with a potbelly stove, to two narrow side-by-side rectangles, the entrance on the right just a few paces beyond the gas pumps. One room was dedicated to food and the other to most everything else—at least loosely anyway. Shelves beyond the entryway were stocked with canned beets, corn, Karo syrup, flour, sugar and cornbread mix, buns, and bread. The food was interspersed with Palmolive dishwashing soap, Brillo pads, matches, and butane. Beer, milk, and frozen goods filled cases lined along one wall, and the Goldhardt deli case occupied the far back corner, stocked with ham, sausage, hamburger, Trail bologna, pickle loaf, and loads of different cheese rounds. Fresh produce and fruits were crammed into one refrigerated case—pineapple, tomatoes, lettuce, peaches, grapes, and green onions—a bit of everything, usually a collection of whatever happened to pass Loany and Maxine's scrutiny at the farmers' market.

Beyond the cash register, located stage left, a ramp led up into the second room flanked by a large glass display case on the far side wall. It spilled over with cookie jars and glass knickknacks and was topped with battery-operated cars, clown popping banks, trains, dolls, and games. A refrigerated self-serve floor chest and upright bottle vending pop machine served up every flavor of soda imaginable—Coca-Colas, A&W Root Beer, 7-Up, Creme Soda, Orange Crush, Pepsi, Choc-ola, and Vernor's Ginger Ale. Dungarees, shirts, and work gloves hung on the front wall crammed in with fishing poles, flies, nets, and worm and crawler bait. Flashlights dangled below a shelf filled with gas lanterns. Beer signs were suspended from the ceiling along with Frito Lay sales banners and Coca-Cola posters. Like Paradise Rice, there was a little something for everyone at Goldhardt's Grocery.

Among the organized chaos was the country store's premier feature, at least to the area kids. Tucked inside the entryway a few paces to the left stood a humongous candy case, a three-tier wood and glass monster Loany painted up all white and antique gold. The shelves spilled over with dozens of different goodies all arranged according to price, from penny candy all the way up to nickel candy bars. Among the possibilities were root beer barrels, candy necklaces, bubble gum cigarettes, jawbreakers, and red hots. Tootsie Rolls, wax lips, Zagnuts and Black Cows competed with Necco Wafers, Mars Bars, lollipops, Milky Ways, and Snickers.

After school ended each year, our first trip to Goldhardt's Grocery was the mother lode of sugar buzz and cavity building. My friends and I scoured the ditches while we walked the two and a half miles down our country road to the store, searching for beer and pop bottles to convert to candy cash. A winter's worth of casual car window littering reaped huge rewards. Pop bottles earned us two cents and beer bottles three, and we cheered each time anyone spotted the glimmer of brown glass in the ditch.

"What have you got?" Loany asked as we burst into the store clutching sacks spilling over with dirty glass bottles. "Okay, that's thirty-three cents each," she declared while scanning over our parcels. "Go on and take them to the back room." Holy crap. Thirty-three cents! I could get three candy bars and still have enough money left for tons of penny candy.

The selection process was serious and absolutely daunting. Loany stood waiting with a brown paper sack in one hand while leaning on the case with the other as we made our picks, considering, revising, and then picking again. She filled our orders one by one, content to let us fill the minutes in her day. All customers were important to Loany; even twelve-year-olds with pop bottle money.

Early afternoons were lazy times at Goldhardt's Grocery in the late sixties, and that is the time of day we usually found Loany minding the store. It seemed to be her shift, though it was tough to keep straight how she, Maxine, Bob, and eventually Okie parsed out the work schedule. Bob opened up weekdays and sipped on beers he hid in the back room before leaving to work second shift at the General Motors plant. Okie manned the early hours on weekends and closed many nights, always impeccably attired in dress slacks, sweater, or sharp-creased button down with a tweed touring cap atop his wavy silver hair. Loany and Maxine made trips to town for supplies and filled in the blanks in the schedule. Maxine inventoried and stocked the shelves, did the bookkeeping, and played the steady eddy watcher of the business.

This left Loany free to be her perpetual fart in a twister, to dabble in a little bit of whatever met her fancy or anything she saw that needed done. She handed out candy on Halloween in costume and lobbed eggs at the cars of teenagers passing by, intentionally missing most of the time but occasionally making contact anyway. She visited with the occupants of the automobiles that were parked in front of the gas pumps or squeezed into the short drive beside the store. Hanging out, er, rather working at the store was Loany's conduit to the larger world and happenings beyond the confluence of the Darbys.

The foursome fell into a rhythm and time marched into the seventies with Loany and Okie earning a paltry living compared to their glory days of gambling, racketeering, and horse racing. They needed money to live on, but how much remained a mystery. Some said the Rices had squirreled away several hundred thousand dollars from their gambling businesses. Others insisted there was nothing, which seems likely, or Loany would have taken charge of Butsy's care and thrown wads of money at a legion of doctors.

As Ollie and Gwenzora Goldhardt slipped into ever failing health, Maxine and Loany administered to them at their home next to the store. Ollie traded in his cane for a walker, and eventually a wheelchair after he lost a first and then second leg to the diabetes. In good weather he sat out in front of the store with a newspaper and flyswatter, waving at passersby and smacking at flies. Gwenzora was content to watch the world go by from her porch glider swing, always in full Sunday dress, perfect hair and makeup and done up in five pounds of elaborate jewelry.

As they faded into the background, Loany helped her parents in every way. She fed and dressed them, and kept track of their medications. She put them to bed at night and led them to the bathroom Okie Rice built that put the trusty outhouse out of business. Loany swore when one of them didn't quite make it to the indoor plumbing.

"For Christ's sake," she said to Maxine after finding a trail through the dining room leading to the toilet. Maxine mused out loud about what they should do now that their parents were nearly bedridden.

"Well, we can't gas them," Loany snapped back in exasperation. Nor would it occur to the sisters to ever put their parents in a nursing home, despite the fact Loany was nearly old enough to occupy a space alongside them. Perhaps it was their German heritage or their practical country roots; people simply took care of their own. They transformed the dining room into a private two bed nursing unit and watched over the Goldhardt patriarch and matriarch until their time on earth ended.

Ollie and Gwenzora died within a year of each other, and Loany and Maxine became official owners of the store. Loany's immediate world had diminished in reach significantly, home base now defined by the boundaries of Paradise Rice and the one hundred odd paces up Alkire Road to Goldhardt's Grocery. Our collective access to Loany's world, however, mushroomed and blossomed tenfold.

***

I don't remember whose idea it was, but Julie Frericks and I found ourselves bypassing a candy stop at Goldhardt's Grocery one fine summer day when we didn't find Loany there. We loped up the steps to Paradise Rice in search of her, quite intent on executing our planned adventure. We were the only school-aged girls for miles on our sleepy county road outside Georgesville. As natural tomboys we gravitated together as friends and comrades in our country neighborhood, filled with boys, where play was defined as poking around in the creek, or using dried cow piles as bases for softball. A turned up nose framed with freckles offset Julie's dark and wavy pixie cut, and her face radiated a youthful beauty and innocence. Beneath, however, was the gifted mind and keen wit of a born wheeler-dealer whose mouth could spit words as lightning fast as her brain strategized them. Julie's stamina and commitment to the art of persuasion was remarkable. She locked in on her target—my mom, her mom, whoever—with focus and zeal until the person usually caved in and permitted us to do whatever she was selling.

Julie stood looking down at Loany earnestly and launched into her pitch without taking in oxygen for several sentences.

"Margie said you would let us ride White Socks. I have a horse, you know. I'm a very good rider—you can ask my dad. Margie rides him too...all the time. Our moms said it was okay as long as you said so. We promise to be real careful."

It was a simple first round for Julie, but one that covered all the basics: experience and skill, parental permission, safety, and the nice touch of offering a referral.

Loany waited patiently for Julie to stop talking, seemingly unimpressed by her patter. Quite unnecessary.

"Sure you can ride him. Go on over to the barn. The saddle and blanket are hanging outside a stall. Take some carrots over with you. There's some in the fridge."

Julie was shocked—she hadn't even needed to escalate to round two. "I told you she would let us ride him," I said, with a satisfied grunt.

Loany didn't size up the world with a more traditional eye of caution. Her boundaries were broad and generous compared to most adults in my realm, and she extended her viewpoint to the children who surrounded her. There was no squelching of ideas or dreams when with Loany. Most all notions were open for execution, often with her in tow to share in the adventure.

As we walked up the drive toward the stable, I spied White Socks out in the corral. He was quite uninterested in us initially. *Ah, wait a minute. Carrots. Maybe I should go over and take a peek.* The handsome bay met us at the fence and munched away contentedly. White Socks certainly looked much taller than I remembered. In fact, he looked bigger than any horse I'd ever ridden by myself. But he was considered a pacing pony, a smaller steed Loany had adopted after Okie had no use for his help training racehorses. As a young child, I had sat atop his saddle while my dad led me around the corral to just let White Socks wander around wherever he chose. Pacing pony or not, standing looking up at him now, he was substantial to a twelve-year-old. As we stepped inside the corral, White Socks took a few paces backwards and then returned to the carrots.

"I'll hold him here, and you go get the bridle and saddle," I commanded. I reached up and grabbed his halter with one hand while offering snacks with the other. "Hurry up. I'm almost out of carrots."

Julie slipped the bit and bridle in place and threw the blanket up over White Socks' back. *Hmmm. That was easy.* The horse was amazingly cooperative so far. But as Julie hurled the saddle toward his haunches, White Socks took two side steps with his back legs. The saddle hit the ground. He continued to munch the carrots. *This girl is no threat whatsoever.* Each time Julie tossed the saddle, White Socks sidestepped it. His maneuver pulled me around in a circle with him, his butt leading the dance. I struggled to keep my hand on the bridle.

"Margie, hold him still," Julie snapped. "How am I going to saddle him if you keep moving around?"

"I'm not doing anything," I replied. "You're the one missing. Look, this isn't working, so let's just forget it." White Socks raised his tail and took a hearty and smelly dump. "I swear if I get that on my tennis shoes, you're cleaning them," I said, pointing to the greenish brown goop on the ground. I swatted at a fly attracted by the smell of horse dung.

Julie motioned toward a hay wagon outside of the corral. "Let's take him over there and I'll get on from the wagon. I can just ride him bareback. I'll get on first, and you can sit behind me."

"I dunno." I was beginning to have serious doubts about our equestrian experience. White Socks, on the contrary, seemed quite pleased to be outside the corral. He allowed me to lead him over to the hay wagon, while keeping one eye aimed on each of us.

Julie leapt up onto the wagon and grabbed the reins. The horse shuffled back two paces and then reared up on his back haunches. I could feel my feet leaving the ground as a sharp and excruciating pain shot down my shoulder and arm. My hand was stuck between the bridle and White Socks' head, and at roughly eighty pounds, I flopped around like a trout on a stick. As White Socks' front legs slammed back down to the earth, I scrambled to regain balance and free my hand. He immediately reared back up with me attached and flailing. This time when he landed, my hand shot free, and I stumbled to stay upright.

The pain in my shoulder took my breath away. My head was ringing. Bent over holding my arm, I gasped, "Where is he? Where's White Socks?"

By now the pacing pony had trotted several yards away from us and was sizing up his options. *Hmmmm. Corral to the right, fence row to the left, and railroad ridge behind.*

That leaves straight ahead past that sniffling girl and down the driveway to freedom.

Oh God, I thought. Loany is going to kill me if he gets out. I hunched down like a basketball point guard and tried to cover the width of the driveway with an imposing stance. White Socks took a few tentative steps forward to test me. I shuffled from side to side to show him I meant business.

"Jeez, Julie, try to grab the reins, but don't rush him. If he gets past me, it's all over." I could not imagine catching White Socks if he made the road, and shuddered to consider my fate if the road and a passerby broadsided the horse and sent him to the glue factory.

White Socks wasn't much interested in being captured. He easily out-maneuvered our clumsy advances. I bobbed back and forth between my post on the driveway and attempts to herd him back into the corral. Minutes slowly dragged by with no positive change in our predicament.

The faint sound of crunching gravel behind me sidetracked my thoughts, and I turned to see Loany slowly but purposely walking up the drive toward us. She was in no hurry and apparently unconcerned about the sight before her. There was no anger or look of the slightest irritation on her face. Loany was as cool and calm as the blue pastel shorts and striped blouse she'd tied up that exposed her tanned stomach.

"Come here," Loany called out to White Socks. The pacing pony whinnied and shook his head from side to side. "I said come here," she commanded, while raising an outstretched hand. The horse stood still. Walking toward him, Loany smacked his rear end and nudged White Socks toward the corral.

"You horse's ass. Go on. Get in there."

Shutting the gate behind White Socks, she turned to us. "There," she said simply. There was no protracted lecture or stern reprimand. Loany did not terminate our riding privileges or dole out a punishment. Nor was there a promise to have a word with our parents.

"Now you can go on and ride him." She chuckled softly.

"That's all right." I spoke up before Julie got any crazy ideas.

"Are you *sure* you don't want to ride him?" Loany's mouth pursed in a grin she was trying to hide. We both shook our heads no. "Okay then. I have to get up to the store so Bob can go to work."

* * *

Sure, she needed to "get up to the store." For as much as Loany needed to get to Goldhardt's Grocery most every day to pull her slot on the work schedule, she routinely looked for every conceivable way to get *out* of the store. Feeding the ducks was the classic excuse, since their existence was tied to Paradise Rice, at least hypothetically

125

anyway. Food preparation ranked second as a reason to escape. Sometimes a pot of bean soup simmering on the stove needed stirring. On other occasions, it was a ham or pot roast in the oven. The mailman's arrival provided yet one more option for Loany to break out. Of course, looking for her glasses was a great standby, since they were usually missing in action. A bathroom break was always a handy backup in a pinch. The reasons were countless and usually tasks any one of us could have easily done for her, but the thought never occurred, at least not to me.

One sunny summer day not long after my horseback riding misstep, I performed the first of many stints as stand-in store keep for Loany. Gliding my bicycle past the gas pumps I propped it up against the windowsill and rushed inside.

"Margie Anne," she bellowed, looking up as I entered. "How are you today?"

"I'm bored."

"I'm bored," Loany mimicked, lowering her voice to playfully mock me. "How in the world could you be bored?" She shook her head while pointing out the door toward the glorious day beyond the confines of the country store.

"There's nothing to do," I replied with the typical complaint of a twelve-year-old.

Loany shook her head again and laughed. "Are you going to be around a few minutes?"

"Sure."

"Good. Listen, I need to go feed the ducks. You can watch things for me here." No matter that I was a minor who could not legally sell beer or operate a meat slicer. "Open up the pop machine and get yourself a soda." Loany handed me a key. "You can make a sandwich or whatever else you want, too. Now, do be careful with the meat slicer."

She continued to give me instructions while opening the cash register drawer. Loany pulled out most of the bills and stuck them down into her cleavage. "There. That should be enough change. Oh, and if one of the Woods boys comes down here and wants to buy on credit, don't let him." She pulled a box of green carbon guest check books out from under the register. Each had the name of a Georgesville resident inked on the top binding. Extending credit had been a part of the Goldhardt's Grocery business model since Ollie opened the store, and despite my recollection of him as a rather grumpy and mean man, he had the reputation of having a soft side, too. Loany inherited good measures of that compassion and kindness and was hesitant to cut anyone off. She knew some of the poorer families in Georgesville depended on that interest-free credit to get by until the next paycheck. Loany rifled through the box until she found the book she was looking for and scanned down through the entries. "I just can't let them put any more on here until it's paid down some," she said slowly, while adding the tally up in her head. She wrote the total at the bottom of the ledger. I glanced over her shoulder. Dang. Over one hundred dollars.

"Just tell them to come back when one of us is here. I'll be back in a few minutes," Loany called out to me over her shoulder as she left the store.

I didn't need a second invitation to collect up a snack. I grabbed an Orange Crush and headed back to the meat counter. Sandwich and soda in hand, I returned to the front of the store, jumped up on the counter, and waited for my first customer.

A short time later a stocky man appeared in the doorway grinning. "Well what do we have here?" he asked while wiping the sweat from his forehead with a shirt sleeve. "Are you in charge today?"

"Loany had to go feed the ducks."

"I see," he replied with a knowing grin. "Here's three dollars for gas." My first sale.

"Oh, aren't you Ronny Hiermer's girl?" he asked.

"Yes sir."

"I thought so. Tell Ronny that Hud said hello."

"Yes sir, I will." I carefully rang up the gas and stuck the bills in the cash register drawer. This was so much fun, and I couldn't believe Loany left me in charge. Maybe she would stay away for a little while longer.

Another hour passed, along with four more customers and the Frito Lay delivery guy. I opened the cash drawer to pay him.

"Um, I don't think I have enough money to pay you and make change."

"That's all right. Just leave the bill for Maxine, and tell her I'll get it the next time."

I looked around for something to do. Making my way to the back of the store, I found beer and pop bottles scattered everywhere. Fitting them in their tiny storage room was always an exercise in precision and patience, because they were usually crammed haphazardly to the ceiling and blocking their wooden storage crates. First order of business was to clear them out so I could begin the inventory and matching ritual. The smell of stale beer and sugar was strong as I lugged the six-packs and singles out of the room.

Organizing the pop bottles was a breeze since Pepsi and Coca-Cola products were the primary kings of pop. A third stack simply held "everything else." But the beer bottles required more skill in branding and distribution, and I checked through my mental list, not aware such knowledge was an odd assemblage of facts for a kid.

"*Now remember,*" Loany's voice in my head guided me along. "*Colt forty-five goes with Pabst Blue Ribbon, Carling Black Label, and Blatz. Rolling Rock goes with Stroh's. Anheuser Busch and Miller are separate, of course.*" I lost myself in the maze of brown glass. Hmmm. One more Pabst bottle and I'd have another full case. The jingle of the front door's brass bell sometime later, startled me.

I hurried up front to find Doc Kniesly, an early adopter of the aluminum-style pop top, pulling two cans out of the beer case. His habit of breaking six-packs open drove Loany nuts—but the illegality of selling single beers was not her beef.

"Jesus Christ," Loany would belt out, accentuating each word in the Lord's name. "Can't he at least pull them from the same one he did yesterday? Why in the hell does he have to pick a different six-pack every day?"

Doc remained unfazed by Loany's squawking. Each weekday for years he stopped in around four o'clock on his way home from the hospital, where he was a renowned anesthesiologist. His shopping list rarely varied—two single cans of Pabst Blue Ribbon beer and a *Columbus Citizen Journal* newspaper. The two beers filled Doc's ride on up the road home. The newspaper apparently was for filling his head after he parked the car.

Doc handed me exact change. "That's sixty-seven cents with tax," he reported, watching me scan through a price list looking a bit bewildered. He took a deep breath and sighed as he pushed his coal black hair back off his forehead. Doc looked tired and haggard, his narrow face filled with thin, vertical lines. He popped the top of one beer as he stuck the other in a rumpled suit jacket pocket and loosened his tie. He took the first swig before moving away from the counter. "Tell your mom and dad hello," Doc said in closing. I watched him get in his car and drive away. *Dang. If that guy would switch to beer bottles we'd be rich with candy money, because I'll bet he'd throw them out the window before he made it home.*

Well, okay, Doc had made his daily appearance, and it would sure be nice if someone else came in. I'd had a total of six customers in two hours, and was beginning to wonder where Loany had gotten to. I glanced at the wall above the door. It was after four o'clock, and I needed to start home soon. I picked up the phone and dialed Loany's house. No answer. Maybe she was over at Grandma Goldhardt's house. I ran next door to check. Still no Loany. The minutes ticked on, and I finally called Aunt Maxine.

"Where in the hell is Leona?" Aunt Maxine demanded. There was more than a hint of agitation in her voice.

"I don't know. She left around two o'clock to feed the ducks."

"Oh, for Christ's sake." Aunt Maxine sounded like a Loany clone. "Give me a few minutes, and I'll be down."

I wasn't around to witness the fireworks that might have transpired between the sisters later that afternoon. Most likely Aunt Maxine shook her head, unruffled her bent feathers, and went on. Loany was Loany, with her habits entrenched over decades of living, and her style of maneuvering about the world would not be altered by a harsh lecture or sisterly reprimand—with or without cursing thrown in for high drama and emphasis. Loany would be at Goldhardt's Grocery when she chose to, and not be at the store when she chose not to. For Loany, the key to fulfillment in life was having something meaningful to do. Just sitting around was not acceptable, and the long afternoons at Goldhardt's could involve lots of idle time. Loany had to be highly engaged mentally, physically, and socially, or she up and changed her venue.

Wherever I happened along Loany, she transformed me into her moment. We visited together at Paradise Rice while she hosed down the tarmac, dug weeds out of the flowerbeds, or cleaned cobwebs off the wrought iron porch furniture. There were eggs to collect from the hen house and once, a beautiful translucent green and blue peacock feather left behind, to discover. We teetered down Little Darby in a bright red, chrome and wooden speed boat, hugging the shore to check duck nests Loany couldn't get a good eye on from the bank, and carried babies that weren't being roosted to her satisfaction up to a cardboard makeshift home on the front porch. I lugged hay bales across the floor of the stable loft to feed White Socks, and was even more startled than Loany and the horse the time the floor ran out from under my feet, and I crashed down to the ground barely missing Loany's head.

At Goldhardt's Grocery there was sure to be one of her flagship connectivity lessons on the patron of the moment. Canned goods needed marked up and shelved, pop machines filled, loose change rolled, and floors swept. The new toys she brought in from some bazaar or flea market would get batteries and a dry run. I once found Loany wobbling down the road in front of the store trying to ride a motorcycle, while the owner laughed and wiped tears from his face while holding her up. She explained it was one thing she'd never tried in her life and thought it was about time.

I could count on standing in for Loany for a while whenever she left to "feed the ducks". My times there after that first memorable shift all melded into one long movie from the seventies with characters in hippy attire and long hair, along with business men and mothers, farmers, kids with candy cash, and the steady sound of the cash register drawer opening and closing. All in all, things were pretty uneventful, so I was stunned when I learned about the robbery. Well, near robbery.

I imagine the two young men sized up the short old lady with platinum hair and figured she would be an easy mark. And obviously they weren't from around Georgesville, or they would have known Loany wasn't about to go quietly. Loany pulled her hand out from under the counter sporting brass knuckles and punched one robber, splattering his nose all across his face. The other must have figured he was no match for her and ran.

"Punks," Loany told me later when I stopped in to check on her.

"Why didn't you use the gun?" I inquired, referring to the thirty-eight revolver that was stashed at arms-length under the cash register.

"I didn't need a gun. The brass knuckles worked just fine." Loany laughed thinking back. "I guess I messed the one's nose up pretty good."

"Did you break it?"

"Hell yes I broke it." She pulled out the brass knuckles for me to examine. "He bled all over the place. I cleaned him up and gave him some ice while we waited for the police to come."

* * *

When Loany approached me to help her sell the store, I was incredibly flattered but utterly confused. Like most around those parts, I expected Loany and Okie to be permanent fixtures at Goldhardt's Grocery. I envisioned them always there for me, on hand when I stopped by for a Coke or some of Loany's homemade ham salad. I would arrive there to Okie's traditional greeting, "Bay-bay. How are you?" or Loany's hello howl. In one way the store seemed like easy access to ready cash, food and drink—a perfect set up for them. But tending to the business was hard work, along with the obligatory running around to stock it and the constant tending the business that accompanied the life of a country store keep.

As the seventies came to a close, Loany had already moved on to her next career, and Okie was approaching eighty years of age himself. She had grown quite tired of the store's perpetual noose. The eternal entrepreneur and street smart dealer, Loany had it all planned out. Her instincts returned her to the one role she knew best, that of playing "the bank." Financing the mortgage would earn more than an outright sale and give her and Maxine some steady income for ten or fifteen years. A buyer and fifty-five thousand dollars later, the sisters handed over the keys, building, and contents in return for a down payment and their mortgage note.

Times were changing in other ways, too. The Columbus Metro Parks had been steadily creeping westward toward Georgesville, gobbling up land around the confluence of the Darbys. Loany and Okie knew they would eventually be forced to give up Paradise Rice, and once again Loany's instincts kicked into play. When the park guys approached them, she said she was happy to sell without a fight, provided they allow her and Okie to remain in the house and use the land for the remainder of their lives.

Loany's proposition seemed like a great idea to the park guys, and they quickly wrote the Rices a check. Why not? The old man was certain to die anytime, and the old woman surely couldn't live that many more years, right? Wrong. It would be another two decades before the Lord claimed the Rices or the Columbus Metro Parks claimed Paradise Rice. As usual, Loany had negotiated herself one whale of a deal. Or rather, "hell of a deal," as she'd surely have put it.

CHAPTER 8

Five Thousand
Bottle Rockets

"Where's the hose?"

—Anonymous

The Fourth of July was screaming toward me full bore before I realized I had zero fireworks in my possession—not that fireworks were legal in Ohio during the seventies and eighties. They were quite illegal and still are, but back then the one particularly important difference from today was there were no in-state outlets to purchase them from and promise by way of signature (and a nod, nod, wink, wink) that you were taking them out-of-state. No, about the only way to do a homegrown fireworks show in Ohio then was to have snagged them en route to a Florida vacation, somewhere down South along Interstate 75 at Joker Joe's or Leapin' Leema's in one of those laid back, hip states that hadn't abandoned traditional

American values—at least when it came to fun. Unless, of course, you knew Loany.

Every year from early May until they ran out, Paradise Rice was transformed into a clandestine fireworks business. The sun porch overlooking the Little Darby became Loany's showroom, with sample product nestled about proudly among the coconut shrunken heads, driftwood, and seashells. Behind locked door the drive-under garage doubled as her warehouse and stored enough raw TNT power to blow Paradise Rice clean up, or maybe more appropriately, all to hell.

Loany's fireworks racketeering business would withstand well the scrutiny of an MBA case study exercise. Like Goldhardt's Grocery, it emulated the oldest and most basic of business models, the "store keeper," and this particular product niche, albeit illegal, was a nice addition to the already eclectic offering in the country store.

Her value proposition was simple: it was all about offering fun, the kind kids of all ages smiled thinking about and the type not easily obtainable, or most certainly not accessible on a daily basis. It mixed that fun with a hint of danger, from a technology standpoint, and the possibility of getting busted by the local law, along with the exquisite beauty of the blast and a steady hint of patriotism thrown in for good measure. Fireworks *are* the Fourth of July. Their appeal is so wonderfully universal, transcending race, culture, gender, age or any other labeling identifier, and that meant Loany's customer prospects were far-reaching. However, she did have one sacred business tenet—no sales to minors, never, ever, under any circumstances. Well, okay, unless Loany specifically knew the parent and a discussion had occurred eye-to-eye, phone-to-phone, or some way other than third party.

Her business may have been illegal, but Loany was not stupid or without principle. Responsibility and safety did outrank profits, unless she stood at the other end of the fuse. The day Loany lit an M-80 and tossed it into Aunt Pat's swimming pool Aunt Pat was not remotely amused, since she happened to be lying on a raft relaxing at the time. The above-ground metal pool made an outstanding blast canister. The force of the detonation shredded the plastic pool liner, and the complementary three-foot water geyser knocked Aunt Pat off her raft.

"Jesus Christ," Loany explained to me later. "I don't know what all the fuss was about. I told Patty I'd buy her a new pool liner."

For the most part, Loany reserved scientific experimentation and routine high jinks to family settings and kept such tomfoolery apart from her business model. Loany's marketing mix—product, price, promotion, and place, was well thought out and sufficient to garner sustainability. As far as product offering went, Loany had every type of firework a customer might request, including several different brands, each exuding subtle differences. A friend who owned an airplane graciously loaded her up when his travels took him near one of her preferred wholesalers.

Cakes, with hundreds of tubes fused together and sequenced, created a barrage of bangs, whistles, pops, and cracks. Garden-variety bottle rockets were on hand for the kids as well as monster rockets that traveled hundreds of feet into the air, their sparkling tails lighting up the night as they ascended. Loany carried flares that produced intense lights and lots of smoke, and fountains that spewed glittering colored fire. There were shells that fired missiles from their mortar barrels, the baby version of big city fireworks displays. Stationary and flying wheels that took off like a UFO were on the shelf in all shapes and sizes along with Roman candles that shot flaming balls and stars. Smoke bombs and fire crackers of every variety rounded out Loany's public offering. M-80s were doled out to the closest of friends and family, kept in private reserve like fine wine.

Loany's market was virtually unlimited, or at least large enough to service her revenue needs, thank you very much. She did not exploit her distinct competitive advantage of having virtually no competition, and I do mean nada. Loany insisted on pricing product fairly and reasonably. Rich or poor alike would find affordable fun in her not-so-secret hideaway, because in point of fact, Loany's mission statement was as much about sharing fun as it was about making money. Her advertising strategy was singular in scope and cheap—word of mouth.

Georgesville was still somewhat remote and tucked away in farmland beyond the western fringes, yet it was easily accessible to a rapidly expanding Columbus, a city working hard to shake its "Cowtown" nickname and image. Goldhardt's Grocery was a perfect front and served as a handy distribution conduit to her retail fireworks market. Just as slot machines had been tucked out of sight years before, a limited offering of the smaller pop power was hidden under the counter or in the back room with the empty soda bottles.

Using a distributor's model Loany sold to a "known" and certified entity, though the familiar rep could bring additional customers along. Some buyers stopped by the country store first, and, if all checked out, were redirected down the road to Paradise Rice where they could purchase from the complete product offering. Business remained quite brisk, particularly as Independence Day drew closer, and a steady stream of cars pulled onto the tarmac and then disappeared a few minutes later, their occupants clutching brown paper bags filled with goodies. That bag was not the lone clue Loany wasn't distributing something like illegal drugs out of her sun porch; a number of Columbus city police officers were also some of her best customers.

I pulled into Paradise Rice near dusk and set out to find Loany. She came out of the house, bamboo purse draped over her arm, lipstick bright red and fresh, wearing white short shorts, tanned bare legs exposed, with leather sandals and a Hawaiian print shirt. A necklace of small seashells and parrots finished off the ensemble.

"Hey Loany, I need some fireworks. Is it after hours?"

"No," she laughed, "there are no set hours for family."

I introduced my friend as we stepped into the sun porch and began rattling off my order—a couple boxes of Roman candles, half dozen packs of bottle rockets, two packs of firecrackers, and a pack of those things we called whirly gigs—the round spaceships that spin into the air and spew sparks.

"You mean satellite wheels," Loany suggested.

"Yeah, okay," I mumbled. My detailed recollection of product names had slipped over the years. I added some smoke bombs, sparklers, and began searching for anything else safe younger kids could enjoy with my adult supervision. "What were those things that grow into a snake or something like that when lighted?"

"Now, kids like these poppers, too." Loany directed me to a case of tiny yellow boxes that could have easily doubled for a pack of gum. "They're perfectly safe. Just throw them down on a hard surface and they crack and pop. Do you want any mortars?"

"No, nothing high-end like that right now. I just need some things to entertain the kids staying at Mom's after the family reunion." I finished off my order, paid Loany, and as she stuck the money down in her cleavage, she glanced at her watch.

"Come on with me," Loany more ordered than asked. "Tommy Tong (name changed to protect the guilty) is shooting off five thousand bottle rockets, and I don't want to be late."

Five thousand bottle rockets? Five thousand bottle rockets would take until Halloween to let off. Why would Loany care to watch that, and how can I get out of this? Spending hours watching some fool let off bottle rockets was way not how I intended to spend my evening.

As if reading my mind she added, "All at once, Margie Anne."

Oh how I hated being called Margie Anne. A formal Margaret Anne was my parents' *you-are-in-big-trouble* convention, or Margie did fine for everyday use. Margo was even an okay nickname my work friends tagged me with, but Margie Anne was my nails-on-the-chalkboard moment. I shot my friend a stern look—*don't you ever use, repeat, or even insinuate the label Margie Anne to anyone, or you shall die.*

"He's firing all five thousand off together. Won't it be great?" Loany added, her mouth accentuating the first word as she contemplated the sight. "I got them for him, and he spent the past three days setting up the display."

Good Lord. Five thousand bottle rockets would cost quite a bit of dough, and I pondered the math to calculate a rough estimate. Let's see, Loany sells them for a dollar twenty-five per dozen...that's like five hundred dollars. Holy crap!

"Who is this guy?" I asked. "Where does he live?"

"Up across from the golf course." She repeated his name again, and it still meant nothing to me.

"Now, you remember Chick Green, right?" I nodded. So far so good. "Chick's sister, we all called her sis, ran around with your father's mom. Now, her uncle, you remember the one-armed school bus driver don't you? Well his son...."

I half-heard her as Loany continued, but my mind had not processed past the first branch of her connectivity tree. Wait a minute. Did I just hear something about a one-armed bus driver? How can he drive a school bus with one arm?

Skipping forward three reference points in Loany's chronicle, I struggled to catch up with her connectivity lesson, one that always included relatives who were dead before I was born, others I hadn't seen in twenty years, and a few native country folk. And Chick Green—somehow this Chick Green lady showed up in every connectivity wishbone diagram. Years later I would become absolutely convinced Chick Green was the six degrees of Kevin Bacon in Georgesville, Ohio.

"One-armed bus driver?" I repeated her comment aloud now, more as a reference point of where my mind had stalled than as a question.

"Yes. He had the route out past Lilly Chapel. He came into the store all the time," Loany added, like this data point would clear up everything.

Making the human connections of a person's life was an extremely sacred ritual to Loany. The definition of an unknown individual equaled the sum of those coming before and those who surrounded one in the present world. That was Loany's math, and she was determined to continue until she was satisfied her student had closed the links and shared in the familiarity. I knew from experience we weren't through yet.

"Okay. You know Woody and Nadine," Loany stated as fact.

"Yes." I definitely did know who they were.

"Now you remember Tootie," Loany said with certainty. "Always came to the fish fry," she added for good measure.

What did Tootie have to do with Woody and Nadine? What do all these people have to do with the bottle rocket guy?

"Just follow me in your automobile." Loany sighed, apparently convinced I was a lost cause. She jumped into

her silver Lincoln Continental and took off up the road,
winding up Graveyard Hill past the Oak Grove Cemetery
and bar of the same designation, past where her parents,
two sisters, a brother, son, first husband, and countless
other relatives lay in eternity.

Riding with Loany in a car was a potentially life-
threatening experience, and following behind her in one
not much more comforting. The trailing task brought with
it an unsettling sense of having been granted a front row
premier into the text of one's obituary, had her number
come up with you on board.

*Leona "Loany" Rice, 68, of Georgesville, Ohio, died
suddenly Friday when she lost control of her automobile,
having forgotten she was supposed to be driving it. Her
niece, Margie Hiermer, 29, of Galloway, Ohio, also died at
the scene and was last heard screaming, "Oh shit! Watch
where you are going!"*

When Loany drove a car, she was much more
interested with what was happening outside of it, focusing
way beyond the confines of the task at hand, successfully
and safely maneuvering the vehicle. On this evening, she
studied a subject to the far left out of her open window,
across the park field toward Big Darby Creek. Something
had caught her eye off in the distance. Maybe it was a deer
searching to bed down at dusk, or the sound of the creek
waters wandering across limestone and river rock. Perhaps
she was thinking back to times when she was a young girl

and walked the path along the creek, which had been the major north to south thoroughfare to travel between settlements for trappers, Native Americans, and settlers. The trail, long ago grown over and usurped by roads designed to handle the Model T to 300Z, served as a deer run along Big Darby and a trail we snuck around on as kids while playing out of sight of the park rangers.

Loany's car tires spun precariously close to the road's edge, eventually drifting off it a bit, the sound of gravel and sensation of sinking into the ditch edge snapping her back to the present. She made a small jerk and realignment by glancing back to the road for a moment, to make the necessary correction.

"Is she okay to drive?" My friend pointed toward the Continental nervously.

"She's fine," I replied, grinning. I had to admit her car sometimes looked a bit like the driver had been nipping a tad too much of the sauce. But Loany rarely drank any kind of sprits these days, preferring to save her precious moments to drink up life's beauty and joy happening all around her.

"It's just the way she drives. Always has," I added.

Loany's key to eventually surviving nine decades, nearly eight of them behind the wheel, was while she did clip along in her twilight years, she didn't drive so awfully fast she couldn't recover and rebound from not paying attention to the road. Her car looked more like a lazy but determined bumblebee meandering from flower to flower in one general direction. In Loany's case, the two ditches set the upper and lower tolerance in her steering specification.

In fewer than five minutes, we pulled into the driveway of an attractive brick ranch home on a half-acre lot with a golf course beyond the front view and farm fields behind. The lawn was filled with cars tucked everywhere and in every configuration imaginable. They spewed out along the road on both sides, nearly blocking it. Scanning a few houses in each direction, I decided it was too scary along the roadway to park and perfect conditions for a side swipe. I inched into the driveway.

"I don't want to get stuck here all night," I muttered, edging my way into the car throng while studying the options. Eventually I spied a spot mostly in the ditch, but inside the yard proper. I stuck the nose of my RX-7 up against the driveway T-boning the road, confident no one would block the exit. Climbing out of the car, I looked around for Loany. I couldn't see her but did hear, as was typical, her booming voice full and clear above the rest. The sound appeared to come from the vicinity of the house. I knocked on the front door and stuck my head inside.

"Come on," Loany bellowed, motioning to me. "Come on inside here."

I made my introductions all around not recognizing a single face in the crowded room. By the time I finished Loany had trotted halfway out the back door, bored by the mostly girl talk. I followed her outside to find four men huddled in the center of the yard around a large 2x4 and plywood platform that most certainly doubled for an above-ground pool foundation. There on top of the plywood were more bottle rockets than I had ever seen stacked upright in one location. Apparently five thousand, to be exact. What I did not see was one single bottle, beer, pop or otherwise, to launch them from.

Bottle rockets came in cubes of a dozen, easily separated into single units, and I was curious to learn the finer details of this space mission, such as the staging and fit between projectiles. Fuses were discrete for each rocket, and they weren't very long either. How were they tied together, one in each cube, or some other configuration? Were the cubes sitting down inside of a holder? Surely all five thousand weren't threaded into a single serial string? I pondered the setup, becoming more curious about the methodology and strategy to be employed.

Next, I considered whether the idea was for one rocket in each dozen to light the rest. But wouldn't that result in lots of misfires? It also seemed all the concentrated energy might ignite some bottle rockets above the fuse and detonate them at ground level. I took a couple of steps toward the launch platform to satisfy my curiosity, but a quick look from the mission commander suggested this was a proprietary, classified area. It surely was not considered a chick area, not even a chick related to Loany. In respect to the monumental efforts stacked on the platform, I retreated to the chain-link fence that defined the lot and continued to watch from a respectable distance, scientist to scientist. I remained completely intrigued by the bottle rocket launch pad.

Looking around and sizing up the group in the yard, I assumed Mission Control Guy was also the homeowner and master of this amazing display before me. He looked up and waved hello after Loany's introduction and went back down on one knee fiddling around at the corner of the launch site.

I strained my eyes to decipher Mission Control Guy's hand movements, and the setting sun reflected shining wire that crisscrossed the platform in a checkerboard pattern, positioned to hold the bottle rockets in place. It appeared they had been divided into four quadrants, though studying the layout I couldn't easily tell where one ended and another began. The idea then, I presumed, was for each corner of the grid to be lit simultaneously. Three other very serious Mission Control Assistant Guys were standing by, talking in hushed voices.

Someone from the house yelled out from an open window. "How much longer? Tell us when you're ready."

Dusk's premier to the night was in place now, a nice one to render up a spectacular exhibition. Mission Control Guy finally stood up, apparently satisfied with the launch pad, and announced the show was soon to begin. I concluded that my post leaning against the chain-link fence was a good one and watched as the four blastoff guys knelt down and flicked lighters.

Individual rockets began to zip up and crack into the night sky, all eyes turned upward, the gallery smiling at the red and gold sparkled trails of fire.

Houston, we have booster ignition and lift off. Returning to space and paving the way for future bottle rocket missions beyond.

But almost immediately, the sound of one bottle rocket could not be distinguished from any other. The continuous zipping of the trajectory into the sky competed hard with the ongoing crack of detonation. The noise level escalated rapidly, and it was not pleasant.

Houston, we have liftoff, but it didn't roll up in a very neat package.

Countless rockets had been firing for over a minute, and smoke covered ground zero to middle space, rising about twenty-five feet in the air. With very little breeze, it had stalled right above the backyard, quite content to go nowhere. I strained my eyes to see anything but did not question the bottle rockets were still firing, as the noise continued to be deafening. I stuck a finger in each ear. It was becoming harder to breathe without choking. With the smoke stalled out, it took a while for anyone to notice countless rockets were not drifting across the street onto the golf course as planned, but rather, they were plinking down in rapid succession right on top of the roof of Mission Control Guy's house. Some swerved off course, low flying and erratic, never completing their intended journey into space, and hit the roof a split second after ignition. The more timid members of the gallery began to make a dash for the safety of the house.

A window opened up and a not too pleased wife-type voice shot out, "The roof—are they hitting the roof? You're going to burn down the house. Stop it!" But what had been put into motion could not be stopped.

Houston, we definitely have a problem here.

Roger, copy that Mission Control Bottle Rocket Guy.

"Where's the hose?" someone yelled. And, at that moment in sheer simultaneous group revelation, several of us looked in the direction of the front yard where our cars were parked.

"Oh my God, they're probably hitting the cars." A woman disappeared toward the front of the house, and no one waited for an answer to her proposition. The collective conscience of the crowd kicked into enlightenment-mode, and we charged the side gate to the chain-link fence, fighting to push through it simultaneously.

As I awaited my turn, I glanced toward the porch in search of my sidekick, but instead, spied Loany leaning against the back of the house. Alone. Hands in pockets, grinning, watching the crowd go crazy, amused at all of us. And then still grinning, she tucked her head down, like a school kid caught in a prank and trying to distance herself from the evidence at hand. Maybe someone would remember where all these bottle rockets came from in the first place. Loany shot a look over her left and right shoulder, locked eyes with me for an instant, and disappeared into the smoke-filled backyard.

I reached the car about the same time my friend did, and we were out on the road before most anyone else had sorted through the car mess. The amber glow from the continuing pyrotechnic chaos reflected playfully into my rear view mirror, punctuated by the crack of the bottle rockets continuing to fire, as we left the screaming and pandemonium behind.

"Who owns the blue Ford? We need it moved now!"

"Have you seen Tammy? Get her out here."

The sound of laughter next to me overtook that of car doors slamming and engines turning over as I wound the sports car effortlessly through five gears. I turned to look at my passenger. She shook with laughter, coughing and wiping her eyes to get a grip. She opened her mouth to speak but gave in to an uncontrollable belly laugh and put her head down on the dash. She was still laughing when we reached the top of graveyard hill by the Oak Grove Tavern. And she still couldn't contain herself as I maneuvered the RX-7 across Big Darby bridge and downshifted into fourth gear just before Little Darby bridge, slid the back end of the car around to make a hard right turn on Gardner Road, and buried the tachometer heading toward home.

CHAPTER 9

Tickies

"I'm really not sure of my name...
Granny Rice says it's Jackass."
— Resident, Orient State Institute

During a quiet conversation in 1979, Loany told me the thing she was most proud of in her entire life was working with the tickies. She wasn't talking about conducting a scientific research study on Lyme disease or referring to the common wood tick found on dogs. Loany wasn't waxing adoring for the profession of entomology and all things creepy crawly. Nor was she labeling the act of scalping concert or sporting event tickets. When Loany spoke of her tickies, she was referring to the mentally disabled children at Orient State Institute.

Loany placed this one life event above all else she had accomplished to that point, and it withstood the test for all her years on earth ever after. Her tickies outpaced the universal roles of daughter, sister, or wife. Tickies edged out the very serious task of helping raise the Goldhardt family orphans—my father, and his cousins, Judy and Jimmy. Her tickies were in a class alone beyond even all the leagues of kin who stayed at Paradise Rice whenever times were rough financially, they found themselves suddenly single, or were simply drifting along in life.

Loany's tickies were much more important to her than the countless good deeds that came so naturally—ignoring debts owed at Goldhardt's Grocery, slipping money to anyone in need, or even more simple acts of kindness. One day an admirer complimented a watch Loany was wearing when the two ran into each other at the local farmers' market; a few days later one just like it appeared in the admirer's mailbox. That was typical Loany, even in her eighties when she had little, if any, money to spare. And when it came to the reflection back over a life full of achievement and rich variety, that self-accounting of the standout moments a person takes the most pride in, ticky time usurped her years as a rich and infamous numbers racketeer, too.

On this particular day when I visited Loany, I was on a mission. Fall quarter of college was starting in two weeks, and I had come armed with spiral notebook, pen, and question set. I just knew Loany would make great material for some of my advanced journalism classes. She seemed surprised when I called and asked if she would be my subject.

"You want to interview me?" Loany asked with a chuckle, and then continued before I could answer. "Hell's bells. Come on down any time."

When I arrived at Paradise Rice, she was relaxing in the living room, leaning sideways on the arm of a divan, legs pulled up and tucked to her side. This was a preferred lounging position and one that placed Loany in proximity to the telephone, a most important home time requirement. For when Loany did manage to sit still for any length of time, there was usually a phone attached to one ear, her earring set aside for her to misplace later. She could yak on and on taking notice of, and offering appreciation for, even the most mundane of details in the other's life.

After ending a call, she always shared the identity of the person to whom she had been speaking on the other end of the line, whether her visitor was interested or not. Invariably this would lead to another rousing identity recognition and connectivity discussion for me to fail miserably, when I was Loany's company.

Oh no, here we go again. No Loany, I do not know that person. Swear to God. No, I don't know Aunt Tildy's brother-in-law. The one whose sister ran around with the Henson boys. Oh, wait a minute. Whoa. I just heard Chick Green's name. Repeat, Chick Green has officially landed a spot in Loany's connectivity wishbone diagram.

But on this day I lucked out, as there was no teleconference in process when I arrived. The television droned in the background, more for company than content. Loany didn't spend much time in front of the television. She preferred a life filled with action and events rather than one of mere spectator.

I got started with my very serious line of questioning. She interrupted me.

"Turn that TV off," Loany directed, while pointing toward the box. "You know I can't read or watch anything on the trial." I looked back at her blankly.

"The trial?"

"The Ucker trial," Loany bellowed back at me with a look of utter disbelief. "I'm a juror on the Ucker murder trial," she repeated for emphasis. How could I not be aware of her role and local notoriety in this event?

Despite spending most of my time in the rural foothills of the Southeastern section of the state at Ohio University, even I knew the story behind the Ucker trial. College was a place and time where the world was deliciously small and certainly insular, with a traditional seventies focus on beer, books, and bongs. So naturally, it was also quite easy to lose sight of any world outside the foothills of *Harvard on the Hocking,* as OU was known. *Disco? What is this thing people are talking about? Never heard of it.*

But everyone had heard of the Ucker murder trial. While most tales of jury duty consist of working endless crossword puzzles interlaced with trashy novels, copies of the *Enquirer*, and mind numbing boredom, Loany had managed to land on the jury of the century in Ohio.

This particular murder trial had all the drama and ringside analysis of a *Court TV* event along with the trappings and plot curves of a double episode of *Law and Order*. And amazingly, it occurred so many years before either had been conjured up in the minds of striking television writers. Here in reality, life was much, much better than art.

The Ucker trial was a real life story of tragedy with some sex and drugs, high society and low society, black people and white people, and mobsters all thrown in together. Added to the mix were several nice soap opera touches. There was a mystery woman, a love triangle, and plans of torture and mutilation. In a town with a handful of murders a year, this one was scandalous and this one was Hollywood huge. The trial particularly captured the interest and riveted the community because one man was black, one white and both physicians. And it pit the word of a convicted peddler and bank robber with ties to the mob against a seeming pillar of the community.

The victim was a prominent African American physician, Dr. Walter Bond, who was gunned down gangland style in front of his office on Halloween, in 1977.

The alleged mastermind behind the murder was white physician-attorney Dr. David Ucker, chairman of a hospital's obstetrics and gynecology department, and the deputy county coroner. The plan was to kidnap Bond so Ucker could castrate him. According to the gunman, Ucker was consumed with jealousy and rage over Bond's affair with a white nurse who later dated Ucker, too. So, he hired a trigger man, furnished him with a gun and took him to Bond's office, and waited. When Bond resisted, he was killed.

The jury of six men and six women was selected in just three hours, and Loany must have gotten lucky on the voir dire portion of the tryout. It could have gone real bad for her.

"Mrs. Rice, have you ever had a run in with the law?"

"Well...uh, not officially."

"Are there any persons involved in this case you are personally acquainted with who might prejudice your thinking or decisions?"

"Why, hey-ell no. The judges and cops Okie paid off all have to be retired or dead by now."

"I see. Now Mrs. Rice, have you, a close friend, or relative ever had a bad experience of any sort with a person of another race that may affect your ability to be a fair and impartial juror in this case?"

"Oh my God, no. The blacks were the best bag men we ever had. Why one gave Okie all of Dayton when he retired, you know."

"That is interesting. However, moving on, what is your opinion of the medical community—toward physicians?"

"I admire and respect the doctors…yes, I do. Well, other than the son of a bitch that cared for my son."

Nevertheless, somehow Loany made the cut, and the judge beseeched the media not to publish the addresses of the jurors, given the volatile nature and high profile of the trial. The local news networks took turns sticking one camera in the courtroom. Hundreds of articles and news stories were aired. The trial was moved twice to larger courtrooms to accommodate a standing room only crowd. And Loany enjoyed every darn minute of it. Of course.

"Now, Margie Anne, I would *love* to tell you more, but I can't talk about the trial with anyone." Loany accentuated the words with a hint of drama and titillating lilt in her delivery.

"Mmm, mm, mm, it is fascinating," she added, and crossed her arms up tight against her chest. "You know, the judge pulled us out and questioned whether we had been discussing it. I looked him straight in the eye and said, 'No sir. Absolutely not.'"

I smiled to myself sitting here now with this woman, the one who had flat out broken the law, written a few of her own, and lived myriad shades of grey bending others.

Loany's morality meter was sharply aligned with the civilized world regarding the act of murder, and she placed great legitimacy with the judge and the authority vested in the court.

"How long do you have to do it?" I asked.

"As long as it takes," she replied. "Who knows? They're saying the judge is going to sequester us. Going to put us up in a fancy hotel downtown close to the court house," Loany added. The idea seemed to appeal to her.

"What about Okie?"

"Oh hell, he'll be fine," she snorted.

"Well, what about your job?"

"They have to let me off work, but I do worry about my tickies. How are they getting along without me?" Loany looked off into the distance.

Loany did not create the "ticky" label, but she did embrace it with hearty enthusiasm. No doubt its origin was not meant as a particularly flattering characterization of the developmentally disabled residents at Orient State Institute by some of those entrusted with their care. But to her, it was an endearing label of love, a pet name for her herd, one to set them apart for the truly special human beings they were in her eyes. Loany did not position or validate her ways and the use of the word in an academic journal article as a successful model for "appropriation," or the process of a stigmatized group revaluing itself from a negative label. In fact, she knew very well her tickies had no idea that term was despicable. Loany did not strike out to raise social awareness and mobilize a public debate and movement with the end game of bold mass empowerment. But what she did know and do most intuitively and from the very core of her soul and essence was to give this group with no voice a resounding validation and positive presence. Since Loany used the ticky brand almost exclusively, everyone around her ended up adopting it, too. As the tickies most unofficial but powerful spokesperson, she unquestionably shaped the image and perception of the children at Orient State Institute.

Landing a job at Orient gave Loany a ready-made universe to thrive in and reign as supreme queen. Stretched across eighteen hundred acres along the Big Darby south of Columbus, the state facility for the "feeble minded" housed three thousand individuals too mentally impaired to be cared for at home, along with those less-so who were forgotten or placed there from within the system. Many lived out their entire lives at the compound.

Sixty buildings filled the grounds along with a massive garden in the rich bottom lands by the river. Cows, goats, chickens, and pigs were raised to help feed the tenants. Dorm-like cottages of different shapes and sizes housed the residents. Some sheltered up to one hundred each, and smaller, more intimate dwellings lodged half that many. Orient had its own power plant, its own waste treatment facility, a central cafeteria, and a hospital. It was like a miniature self-contained city.

This little city required over fifteen hundred employees to sustain it. There were doctors, nurses, cooks, and janitors on staff. Members from various trades roamed the complex, too—plumbers, carpenters, and electricians. Teachers looked after those able to attend in the schoolhouse. Administrators minded after the numbers and business of caring for the mentally challenged.

There was a gymnasium, a four-lane bowling alley, and softball fields for summer fun. And there was Loany.

After visiting the institution, she knew she had found the answer she needed to ease Butsy's death, even if it meant going back to school at fifty-eight.

"Why, it scared me to death...me sitting there with all you young college kids. But when I saw those kids, they just gave me what I needed, and I knew I could give them anything. They could all be my kids."

"Wait a minute. I thought you told me you had an eighth grade education? How did you get into college classes?" I flipped back through my note pad scanning through my scribbles.

"I did only finish eighth grade. They didn't ask, and I didn't tell them," Loany said matter of fact, with a sly smile. Unnecessary, irrelevant details.

As part of the Foster Grandparents Program, Loany's official job was to prepare residents for life on the outside, or to brighten the lives of those who would never live on their own in the outside world.

"I'm a General Activity Therapist," Loany explained to me with great pride.

What the heck is an activity therapist? I thought to myself, and then it hit me. "Damn, Loany. You get paid to play and shop!"

She looked a bit startled by my characterization at first. "I guess I never thought of it that way before," she replied. Her hearty cackle filled the room.

I had never considered Loany a "hobby" person. She didn't amass any one item in particular and certainly couldn't "light" in on any one thing at a time. Loany didn't sew quilts or collect postage stamps. But man was she a shopper, and not an online or a QVC remote control shopper either. Loany was a full-bodied, use all six of her senses to touch, see and smell, be-there-in-person-and-stay-the-distance shopper. She was ready to go anywhere at any time an outing had to do with shopping. Shopping put Loany out and about in the world where she might run into old friends or meet new ones. Loany could shop in evening clothes atop five-inch high heels after attending a wedding or in work clothes finished off with gun boots. Short shorts, poodle skirts or a pajama top, whatever her fashion mood of the moment, shopping offered Loany pure unbridled joy and discovery.

By this point in her life, Loany had mastered shopping at every conceivable price point. She relished the search and hunt whether contemplating the choice between an Asscher or emerald-cut, three carat diamond ring or sifting through dirty junk at a flea market. Littered throughout Paradise Rice were Loany's acquisitions made during the poor years, all jam packed with the finery of decades gone by.

Looking around my immediate spot in the living room, I spied three tiny porcelain frogs next to a brass peacock paperweight. A ceramic sombrero-clad farmer boy was tending a couple of geese up on the television as a glass Siamese cat sat guard, gazing over pictures of grandkids. A wooden duck wearing a frilly doily stuffed with fake flowers crowded a naked cherub lying on her back. A shiny baby alligator and a donkey made of rope wearing an aqua felt beaded saddle and reins were both sitting on an end table next to my chair. On the floor was an impressive brass spittoon, and my book bag was perched atop Loany's legendary footstool—tennis-shoed feet and baggy socked legs balancing a stool covered in olive and gold chenille fabric. Who in the world would buy such a bizarre looking novelty and plop it front and center in the living room? Had I tried to pull off such a fresh approach my friends would have snickered behind my back or laughed right to my front. But with Loany, well, it just worked. There was certainly a lot going on in this room and every other at Paradise Rice.

Loany's tickies were indeed in incredibly good hands. For one thing, when it came to the art of consumerism I couldn't fathom an item a ticky might desire that she had not personally surveyed, researched, or already acquired. But most important, Loany had created a world where all colors, kinds, and classes were brought together to coexist in perfect harmony. She saw the beauty in every little thing and placed equal value upon them.

Loany sat quietly, waiting for my next question.

"I mean, I didn't know that was your whole job," I said, continuing on the pay-for-play score Loany had managed. "I thought you just did trips for special occasions."

"Oh no, I take my tickies with me everywhere."

Loany took her tickies to the mall, to the movies, and Ted Nugent rock concerts. She loaded her tickies up in the van and headed to baseball games and ambled through art galleries, a gaggle of tickies in tow. There were long hikes in one of the metro parks with tickies single file and canoe trips with tickies bobbing along with the current. Loany arranged for her tickies to have a tour of the county jail. The nice thing for Loany was she knew the kids went along only because they really wanted to, since each had to pay his or her own way from earnings set aside from day jobs inside Orient.

"I don't think there has ever been anyone at Orient who has done the things I have done. Those kids know that I care, that I respect them, and I'm not afraid of them. I just tell them, 'I guess you kids will be watching Granny today; Granny won't be watching you.' It builds their confidence and security."

I knew firsthand there was no exaggeration in Loany's proclamation that sometimes the tickies had to watch over her. I'd recently stopped to visit a friend who worked at the local mall. As I plopped down on a chair at the Clinique makeup counter, my friend appeared shaking her head and grinning.

"You just missed Loany," she said. "I heard all this noise by the front door, looked up to see what was going on and there came Loany with dozens of tickies."

"What were they doing?" I asked.

"Oh the tickies were fine. They weren't doing anything wrong," she continued. "Loany was the one carrying on and making all the noise."

"Where were they going?" I wondered aloud. What would Loany do with thirty odd tickies at Lazarus?

"I don't know. They disappeared up the escalator with Loany waving and smiling at me."

So Loany had finally settled into the one job that featured her specials gifts and allowed execution of her signature panache and style. It filled her days while feeding her soul with a happiness and peace she hadn't known since Butsy's death.

Loany's tickies, her beloved tickies. This was the one topic she really wanted to discuss. As the interview sped by, Loany had settled into her here and now. I looked at my watch and realized this was probably the longest amount of time we had ever sat talking one on one, focused simply on Loany. Of all the things we'd been discussing over the hours, she had a fire in her eyes and enthusiasm and passion in her voice beyond her usual one hundred decibel presence. Loany's tickies were her life now and the best that had been offered her in sixty-six years.

Just as much as she loved her tickies, everyone at Orient adored Grandma Rice, too, whether she was dressing up as Mrs. Claus at Christmas or flat out raising hell and telling someone on the staff like it was. Loany would move mountains, if necessary, for her tickies. She would kick ass and take names for her tickies if need be. The "need be" for the "kick ass" part of the equation surfaced shortly after she started the job, because what Loany didn't love regarding Orient were some of the things she saw going on there.

"When I started those kids didn't know what a toothbrush was. I had to clip their toenails and fingernails. Most of them were naked, and I had to bathe one hundred kids in two tubs. So I went and told my boss if nothing else I'd bring in a garden hose. I told him, 'If you don't get those kids showers I'm taking them outside with a garden hose myself.' Well, we got the showers we wanted!"

Loany saw residents shackled down who didn't need to be restrained, and this really torqued her off raw. She just knew it was a ploy used by aides to make their jobs easier. Other tickies were beat and medicated because of allegedly violent behavior. This conduct would not be tolerated on her watch. Loany decided to kick things up a notch.

"Back when things were bad, I wasn't afraid to threaten management with the news media. I said, 'I've seen it, told you about it, you've seen it, now do something about it.'"

"Slow down and let me catch up!" I pleaded. Loany was on a roll, and I was struggling to capture her quotes precisely.

"I saw one boy die from what's going on there," Loany continued. "Another was being given two thousand milligrams of Thorazine a day. Now remember, I'm saying two thousand milligrams. It ended up he had a high IQ and shouldn't have been in the damn institution in the first place. Today he's on the outside and has a good job."

Loany never had a single problem with any of the residents at Orient, and she couldn't comprehend why this was not the standard state of being for everybody who worked there.

"I never raise my voice, and I treat all my kids as individuals. I've been put in charge of kids who require twenty-four hour guard. One boy had a death choke that put a doctor in the hospital and took four others to hold him down. We've never had any problems between us." She sniffed with satisfaction over the statement.

Loany didn't use words like "advocate" or "freedom fighter." She didn't brag about being a voice for those who had none. Loany laid out for me what was to her a simple and straightforward proposition on human rights, the basic respect and dignity owed to others, what she refused to accept, and how she corrected it.

It took Loany eight years and some advanced legislation to make things right for her tickies, and her persistence and patience eventually paid off. She was a natural negotiator, not afraid to take charge, who could give and command respect equally. Bit by bit and battle by battle Loany persevered and prevailed. When forward progress wasn't meeting her satisfaction, she picked up the phone and dialed the governor's office. This time there was no offer of a bribe, but there was a demand for change—change and a better life for her tickies.

And then one afternoon some officials from the state of Ohio stopped by to tour the facility and slap themselves on the back in congratulations of what a fine facility they had provided for Ohio's less fortunate citizens. Loany stood in the background and watched as they walked the grounds. One man reached out and tussled the hair of a young boy. He leaned down and looked the boy in the eyes. "What's your name, son?"

"I'm really not sure of my name," the boy replied earnestly. Thinking a moment he added, "Granny Rice says it's Jackass."

"Shit," Loany mouthed the word while pressing her back against a concrete wall, in an attempt to disappear. She held her breath and waited. The official looked at the boy quizzically, then smiled to the others in his group knowingly and moved on.

* * *

Not long after life was the best ever for Loany's tickies, however, a bombshell was dropped. Dick Celeste, Ohio's governor at the time, decided to shut down Orient. Loany was absolutely devastated. Yes, there was, of course, the loss of a dream job. But her despair came in the waves of worry contemplating what would happen to her tickies. Some, the lucky ones, were placed at other facilities designed to oversee the mentally challenged. A few wound up in halfway houses, while others went to begging in the streets. There were those who ended up in jail, and other very unlucky tickies, went to a facility down in Cincinnati and perished in a building fire.

Loany was faced once again living with the familiar emptiness and ache over Butsy's death. She began to search for the next thing that would give her peace and some pocket money, too.

CHAPTER 10

The Georgesville Fish Fry

*"I just saw Loany in the bingo hall talking to
Madge about her hip replacement."*
—Georgesville Fish Fry volunteer

"Now I'm counting on you and Billy this weekend at the fish fry," Loany stated as fact rather than a question. She had hold of both my arms and was staring hard into my eyes, searching for affirmation.

"I'll get there as soon as I can after school Friday, and I guess I can work Saturday, too. Bill is probably planning to help out," I added, not so sure my brother would be all too thrilled at my offer. I knew I wasn't. "Where am I working?"

"I want you in the pop booth," Loany said with the seriousness of a Sunday mass. "We make good profit on the pop, and I know you can keep up. Is your mother coming down? No one runs the register like her," Loany boasted in admiration. "How she adds all those figures so fast in her head. I'm depending on her, and of course, I know Ronny will work every hour in the fish tent."

"I'll make sure I say something to Mom." That was it. The entire Hiermer family was committed without leave to the twenty-third annual Georgesville Volunteer Firemen's Fish Fry. No way around it. Not with Loany on the prowl.

It sure would be nice for once to just attend the fish fry like all the others who came from miles around each year to dine on fresh Lake Erie perch, burgers and fries, beans, coleslaw, and homemade pies. What a treat it would be to hang out in the dining tent, listen to the live music, people watch, and visit with long lost schoolmates. Instead, my weekend was going to be one long grind of incessantly sticky hands and soda duty while dodging the scads of bees that continuously buzzed the syrup canisters and drifted precariously close to my sting-allergic body.

Every year since 1955 in late May or early June, the volunteer firemen hosted their annual fundraising extravaganza, and most everyone in town had a role in the weekend-long food and funfest. The empty lot behind the community hall and firehouse was transformed into a country carnival, complete with transient workers, rides, rip-off games, and fair food treats. It was the social event of the season and the one occasion for which my brother and I saved our allowance all year long and fantasized about how to spend it.

About half of our money would be set aside for the rides—the "roll-o-plane" rocket was stationed behind the firehouse, and somehow I survived countless runs without projectile vomiting. The giant swings were farthest back in the center of the lot, brushing up next to Railroad Street. On the extreme right, the Ferris wheel towered above the corner of the Community Club next to a huge oak tree we could reach up as we crested the top and smack at the leaves in the branches. Loany sweet-talked the local pretty girls to take turns in the dunking tank and muscle ripped farm boys showed off their fast ball and aim. Kiddie rides filled the middle of the lot and games rowed up side-by-side between them and the back of Community Club. There were Ping-Pong balls to lob into goldfish bowls, balloon and dart games, ball and basket toss, plate break, and ring toss. Even though we grew smarter as the years passed and knew the games were almost impossible to win, we threw our cash at them in conquest of troll dolls, giant stuffed fluorescent striped snakes, monkeys, bears, and cowboy hats with our names written in glitter script.

The main event, the food tent, filled the grass in front of the Community Club, and Loany would invariably hunt down my dad and cajole him into taking a break from frying fish to join in the nail-driving contest on Saturday afternoon that was held next to the strong man ring-the-bell striker game. The old ladies held their seats in the community hall lining up their bingo cards, intent on winning big money. Prizes galore were awarded all weekend, and raffle tickets were five for a dollar. The Fire Chief's voice boomed across the grounds from the speaker system in the command central tent.

"Next drawing in fifteen minutes. Get your raffle tickets and win twenty-five dollars. Don't forget—square dancing tonight at eight o'clock. Rush Thomas will be calling."

We decorated our bicycles with crepe paper, balloons and streamers, and rode them in the parade all decked out in patriotic colors and Uncle Sam hats. Firemen threw candy to kids along the parade route, all one and seven-tenths miles of it, and in later years Loany and Okie led the way in a big shiny convertible as the Grand Marshals. The one and only area forbidden to my brother and me while youngsters was the dice wheel game set up inside the firehouse. Though intended to earn the firemen money, it was still gambling in my parents' eyes and so a no-no.

*　*　*

I really didn't mind helping Loany out. But things had changed so much since I was a kid when the enchantment of the event filled my heart and soul. The carnival rides and games were long gone, and the lot behind the community hall held the food tents these days along with a covered stage to host square dancing and other local talent.

The one thing that hadn't changed so much about the Georgesville Fish Fry over the years, though, was Loany.

She was perpetual motion on patrol, never tied to any one task or station. She fetched cups and supplies for the food tent while visiting with friends along the way, and lassoed a stray worker who'd escaped her recruit while yelling hello across the lot to some person Loany insisted, of course, we all should know, too. There was ice and syrup to stock in the pop booth, money to collect from the dice wheel, and babies to kiss on and hug. The tasks were endless for her to dabble in while she moved round and round the grounds. Runner, social central, queen of the fish fry, Loany maneuvered around and took it in just the way she liked things—incredibly committed and involved, but free and loose.

But even though she floated about the place, when someone was actually looking for Loany, she couldn't be located. She was seemingly everywhere and nowhere at once, appearing and disappearing almost simultaneously.

"I just saw Loany in the bingo hall talking to Madge about her hip replacement," one of us would offer.

"Loany was out front a few minutes ago fussing over Tammy's baby," someone else offered.

"I thought she left to open Goldhardt's Grocery for Frank?"

"She was supposed to be getting me change," I exclaimed from my perch in the pop tent. "I need quarters!"

Of course, when Loany wanted to find someone she was quite skilled, wholly relentless. Later that day she poked me from behind, and I was downright shocked at her ask. With Loany it most surely could have been anything, but this request absolutely floored me, and she wondered if my brother and I would run the dice wheel.

"Maxine and I want you and Billy in there tonight," Loany insisted. I was flattered beyond belief. The dice wheel usually had a pack of men lined up to stand tall, Vegas style, looking incredibly serious and important inside the magic room of chance. "We think the two of you will be good at it," Loany explained. "I want you in there early so you can get the hang of it before Okie arrives later in the evening to spin the wheel. It's usually pretty busy when he's around." Even though Okie had been officially retired from racketeering for twenty years, his name still drew throngs of would-be gamblers. Who wouldn't want to take a hand at gambling with *the* Okie Rice, even at a country carnival?

Later, Okie met us inside the firehouse, all business as he explained the process. The four-foot red wheel held one hundred slots of numbers from one up to twelve. Every other number or so was a two followed by fewer threes then fours and so on up to a couple slots with the number twelve on them. In front of the wheel was a large wooden multicolored die with little axles on two corners that allowed it to roll down a ramp and into a small trampoline structure.

"Time is money. Keep the wheel moving," Okie commanded. "Spin the wheel, set the dice rolling and as soon as it lands, go ahead and swipe all the losers' money off the tables. When the number is called, you can pay the winners while the next roll is spinning."

It seemed pretty simple. My brother and I fell into a rhythm, and for the first couple hours I got the hang of holding my hands inside the nail apron tied to my waist that was full of change to pay off the mostly nickel, dime, or quarter players. I kept a wad of ones in my pocket and threw most of the large bills into the end of the trampoline for safe harbor. We took turns spinning and calling the numbers, and when things got hectic, Bill handled two of the three sides of the betting counters. His six-foot-three inch frame easily covered the area to swipe money off the large orange, red, blue, green, brown, and yellow dots painted on the plywood betting boards that lined three sides of the firehouse.

Loany appeared from time to time to check up on us. "Do you need anything?" she asked while running her hand through the bills to appraise our progress. "Have you kids eaten yet?"

"A Coke would be great," I replied. "I'll eat later."

"It'll probably be much later if you don't eat now," Loany chuckled. She glanced over at a younger boy laying out his nickel. "Don't let the kids play," Loany cautioned. "We could lose our license. Just run them off, unless a parent is with them."

I heard the loud speaker crackle as the Fire Chief fired up the microphone. "Come on over to the firehouse. Okie Rice will be spinning the wheel in fifteen minutes. That's right. Come try your luck with Okie Rice."

I looked out the front of the firehouse. The crowd had steadily grown from the handful we started with, since dinner was pretty much over for most of the patrons. The betting boards were filled two and three bodies deep, and I couldn't imagine many more people squeezing in to place a bet.

Okie appeared at the side door of the firehouse and stepped inside. No hat tonight, he chose a grey poplin summer suit that accented his silver-white wavy hair, and a blue striped shirt with contrasting white-starched collars and cuffs. Gold horsehead cufflinks fused with an elaborate raised "R" held the double French fold of the bright white shirt material. A slate grey and navy double Windsor-knotted necktie complemented dark wingtip shoes.

Okie began spinning the wheel and didn't let up. He nodded and waved to his admirers who hollered out his name. Amid the chaos of waving hands of fans, he stood by, calm and regal, with a dignified smile and twinkle in his eye.

"Four on yellow," Okie called out to a round of applause and whoops of joy from some lucky bettor.

The very few times a twelve hit, the Fire Chief fired up his microphone. "We just had a big winner on the dice wheel—come on over and try your luck with Okie Rice."

I personally didn't think we needed any more promotion. My legs and feet were beginning to ache from standing on the concrete firehouse floor for several hours, and my neck had a crook in it from looking down at the tables. As I glanced up from the betting board, I was met with a sea of faceless arms and hands, people trying to lay bets before the cutoff of each spin. It was getting absolutely nuts, and I struggled to keep up. Whenever I needed more time, I held my hand up and then nodded to signal Okie when it was okay to continue. The evening crept on in an endless maze of numbers, colors, and counting of bills and coins.

At some point after darkness fell upon Georgesville, Okie departed and left us to finish up. Betting had slowed considerably, the crisp night air and darkness a signal to all but the most hearty that the day was indeed over. Loany and Maxine appeared together. "You can come on up to the house and help us count the money if you'd like," Aunt Maxine offered. I couldn't believe it. Bill and I were really a part of the inner sanctum.

We headed up Graveyard Hill to Aunt Maxine's home located across from the Oak Grove Tavern, spread the loot out across her kitchen table, and began sorting. Aunt Maxine, always the organized bookkeeper, had a slip of paper, pen and calculator to record our progress. "Put the ones in stacks of fifty," she directed, "and it's a good idea to check each other. When you've completed a bundle, wrap one of these paper bands around it."

Hunched over our spots at the kitchen table, we lost ourselves in mounds of silver and green, filling change rolls and building stacks of ones, fives, and tens. My hands had turned black from handling the money, a detail that didn't register until after wiping my eyes with them. The kitchen table was covered quickly, and our counting space was all but gone as the clock crossed midnight and rolled into another day. As usual, Loany arrived right about the time we finished. Pile by pile and denomination by denomination, the results were coming in. I had never seen so much change in one spot.

"I've got two hundred and twenty-seven dollars in dimes, wait—that's two hundred and thirty-seven," I called out to Aunt Maxine.

"Billy, how many fives did you get?" Aunt Maxine sat waiting with her pen.

"Four hundred and sixty dollars in fives."

As the last of the piles were reported, we all sat waiting for the bookkeeper to give us the final tally. Aunt Maxine carefully checked over her math. She looked up from her paper. "I come up with over three thousand dollars."

"Is that good?" I looked back and forth between my two aunts waiting for an answer.

Loany and Aunt Maxine's eyes were locked, and Loany had a slight grin on her face. "Yes, that's good. Damn good," she added for emphasis.

"How much do you usually make?" I was working hard to wrap my head around this unknown business model.

"Well," Aunt Maxine began, "we have been wondering why the wheel has not made much money over the past few years." Always the diplomat, she chose her words very carefully, hinting but not quite hitting the point.

"I told you that son of a bitch has been stealing from us for years. This proves it," Loany piped to Aunt Maxine. There was no mincing of words with Loany.

Sticking two college kids on the dice wheel had satisfied their mission quite nicely. Aunt Maxine took back charge of my business lesson. "We thought putting you and Billy in there would be a great way to make the point and send a signal that we are watching."

"Can't there be a bad night?" I still didn't understand the implication of their experiment.

"Every damn night?" Loany snapped. "Impossible. The wheel has to make money. The house can't lose."

I hadn't considered the system of probability associated with the dice wheel. Thinking back to my time in the firehouse, Loany's comment did make sense. Six colors on the die, and most likely twenty slots with the number two on the wheel did certainly seem to give the house some handsome revenue generation potential.

"Who do you think is stealing from you?" I had to ask.

The sisters stared at each other for quite some time without speaking. Aunt Maxine quietly uttered a name in answer, and I was absolutely dumbfounded to hear it. *Him? Mr. Pillar of the community and God-fearing Christian warrior?* The man who always had a kind word and a smile, the one who'd teased me as a young girl while presenting me lollipops? Hmmmm. I had to admit, he was a fixture at the dice wheel every year. As hard as it was to rectify in my mind, I knew the Goldhardt girls would not make a hasty or false accusation.

The deep tanned lines in Loany's face were scrunched tight from first the disgust and then the anger growing within her. She contemplated aloud how much money had been stolen over the years. "That son of a bitch," was all she kept repeating.

* * *

As the years rolled along, Loany's passion and enthusiasm for the fish fry never wavered. It remained a favorite event for her. This was her town, the place on the earth where she'd lived out a life full of adventure, variety, and contradiction. Loany had traveled the country roads around Georgesville in her prime while running numbers and dodging the law, and she drove the same route in later years on her way to the Methodist church she attended faithfully out in Lilly Chapel. These were her people, and this was her fire department. Loany talked on the phone late into the night making plans in the months leading up to the annual fundraiser. Should they find a new perch supplier now that this one raised the prices so high? The coleslaw didn't taste as good this past year. Who was going to run the bingo hall this year? She remained the focal point and muse, the person everyone stopped in at Paradise Rice to confer with, to pick her brain, the all wise, historical scribe full of facts, figures, and ideas. Her innate sense of business set the pace and ruled the occasion. Like she had been so many other times in her life, Loany was indeed the center of the star. She was the fabric that bound together a diverse country community and an event, just as she had united two disparate families, the Goldhardts and the Rices, and just as she had brought liberation to her tickies at Orient. Loany's spirit defined the fish fry. I couldn't fathom attending it and not having her there in the flesh to stamp her indelible signature on the event.

One year, my friend Tony decided to tag along with me after hearing me talk about the fish fry at work. He had met Loany for the first time at my Halloween party the previous fall and was an immediate fan. We found her in the Community Club, uncharacteristically sitting at a card table, holding down a stack of bingo cards that were being blown by one of the floor fans that didn't really cool off the building. It was early Saturday afternoon, after lunch and a few hours before the dinner rush would hit. The parade had ended earlier, and the pace around the grounds was relaxed and casual.

"This is my friend Tony—his sister worked with you at Orient."

"Why yes!" Loany's eyes lit up with recognition as she heard the woman's name.

"You left your Pigmy mask at home today?" Tony teased. Loany laughed and the two fell into conversation on the goings on of various employees they knew in common and their whereabouts since Orient had been closed down. I was quite content to just sit and let the two rattle on and on. The hum of the fans in the Community Club had a nice lulling effect. I could take a nap. Glancing out the open doorway, the bright sun outside was a stark contrast to the dim light and breeze surrounding me. It was cozy here, like a comfortable neighborhood tavern on a warm sunny day, minus the alcohol and jukebox.

"What time is it?" Loany grabbed my arm and pulled it toward her to look at my watch. "I probably better get going. We have a whole busload of senior citizens arriving any time, and I have to help get them settled in." She rolled her eyes and shook her head. "Canes, walkers and wheel chairs, I'm sure."

Tony and I grinned back and forth and waited for Loany to catch up with us. "Just how old are these 'senior citizens'?" I asked. Loany looked at me blankly. "About your age?"

She balked for a few seconds, and then her face shifted up into a wide smile. "Hell's bells. I guess they are!"

When the time came that Loany was no longer able to run the grounds working and socializing nonstop, she kept her presence front and center at the fish fry by becoming part of the entertainment. As a member of the All Ohio Cloggers, she had a spot in the front line, adorned in a patriotic costume—white ruffled above-the-knee skirt trimmed in blue that complimented her still fabulous legs and a bright red top that showcased her still humongous boobs.

Watching Loany clog certainly was entertaining, though probably not in the way she intended. Usually half a step behind the precise cadence and rhythm of the rest of the group, head down with her gaze locked on the feet of the clogger next to her, she worked to catch up and get in sync. She stopped and studied a few seconds, then hopped to get one foot going in rhythm. *Oops, it was time to do the spinning turn; where are we here? Oh yeah, now get the other foot moving.*

Whenever Loany hit a smooth spot in the number, her head jerked back up as she scanned the crowd, a big beaming smile plastered across her face, boobs bouncing and knocking along wildly, and she invariably stopped clogging altogether to wave and chat with a friend. Eventually it dawned on her where she was... *Whoa wait, that's right, I'm supposed to be clogging right now.* Loany danced when she felt like it, and she walked off the stage mid number whenever the mood struck her.

Despite her less than stellar skill, being a member of the All Ohio Cloggers took Loany far from Georgesville to perform first at Disneyworld and later in Austria. She planned and talked about the trip for months prior to the departure date, while others fretted and worried about how Maxine could take care of her octogenarian sister, herself, clog, get some sleep, and basically get by. The plane trip alone was taxing even for a person much younger than Loany. What if she got sick or hurt over there? And just how many Depends will fit in a suitcase?

Marty in particular, had strong reservations about the trip and voiced her concerns to both her father and step mother, but Loany would not be dissuaded. And so, Loany laughed, clogged, and pooped her way across Europe while Maxine grumbled, cleaned up, and fussed after Loany. Back home in Georgesville, Ohio at the fish fry, things were as they always had been. Everyone knew Loany, and everyone loved Loany. There were throngs of friends and family around to watch over her and Okie and help the couple make their way.

But in the months leading up to and after one particular fish fry in the early eighties, there was one burden lying heavy on Loany's heart no one had been able to help make go away. She just had to figure out how to earn some money for her and Okie to live on now that Orient was closed. The few bucks coming in from the store mortgage and the modest state pension Loany just hung on long enough to qualify for, just weren't going to get it. And there was certainly no pension for numbers-running, gambling hall owning, and racketeering horsemen.

She shared her predicament with Doug Sullivan, owner of a local farmers' market.

"Who in the hell will hire a seventy-two-year-old woman?" she asked

"Leona," Doug answered, "report to work on Monday morning."

CHAPTER 11

Migrant Farming at Circle S

"You know, Leona, you're getting too old to do that."
—Doug Sullivan, Circle S Farms

Gliding past the Oak Grove Tavern, I sat up straight on my bicycle seat for the first time in ten miles. Graveyard Hill stretched out before me, a favorite part of the route home to visit my parents. The hill was quite steep and long, and as kids my mother clocked us doing thirty-five miles an hour as we peddled fast and furious on our zero-speed bikes. On this magnificent fall day, I was content to coast along and take in the view around me. Past the two Darbys, Alkire Road climbed back up gently passing Goldhardt's Grocery and disappeared at a sharp dogleg curve into farmland beyond. The railroad trestle peeked through amber and crimson leaves on the maples that lined the Big Darby off to my left, and I spied hikers on the park trail beside the Little Darby on my near right. As I reached the bottom of the hill, I could make out the faint outline of someone sitting on the front porch of Paradise Rice. I detoured past the turn onto Gardner Road that would lead me home and propped my bike against the stone wall next to Loany's garage.

"It's Margie," I called out as I bounced up the steps, two at a time. In a bike helmet, tight black riding shorts, and leather cycling shoes, I looked like any of the dozens of other city dwellers who descended on a sunny Sunday afternoon into "God's Country," known around those parts as Georgesville.

"I knew who you were," Loany replied. "I saw you coming down the hill."

"How in the world did you know it was me? I couldn't even tell who you were from that far away."

"Your legs," Loany stated as if this was the most obvious fact in the world. "You have some damn nice legs." Coming from the woman with the golden gams I was quite flattered. "On your way up to your mom and dad's?"

"Yeah, but I didn't think I was going to make it," I replied.

"What happened?" Loany's brow scrunched up as a look of concern spread across her face. Her eyes scanned my body searching for a sign of physical distress or injury.

"Nothing happened to me," I reassured her. Or had it? My mind still hadn't quite processed the sight I'd seen as I was leaving home less than an hour before. The incident started with a sound as if I'd dropped my keys, but glancing around I found them still in my hand. Turning in circles to figure out what I had heard, my eyes fixed onto a neighbor's entryway that faced my driveway. Sticking out of the large rectangular window well next to the front door were two old lady legs in knee-high hose and the requisite black dress shoes. As I related the comical sight in detail, Loany let out a snort and burst into a big smile. This was just the kind of tale Loany loved to hear.

"*It is okay to laugh,*" I said quickly, more to exonerate myself for telling the story than to give Loany permission. "She's okay."

"Okie, get out here. You have *got* to hear this," Loany called over her shoulder into the living room.

Scotch Rocks, as I affectionately called my nearly ninety-year-old neighbor, had toppled into the deep window well and landed neatly on top of a coiled garden hose with her head and butt wedged between the sides. The stench of liquor was strong as I sheepishly approached, afraid of what I might find.

"I swear it looked like the scene from *The Wizard of Oz* where the house falls on the witch," I said earnestly.

"Jesus Christ," Loany managed to choke out between cackles. "What did you do?"

195

"I told her to stay still and called the squad."

When the paramedics arrived, I met them at the street and explained they were about to see something that was going to totally mess with their heads. Loany howled with laughter as I continued my story, and when she got tickled, her mind put her entire body in motion. Wiping her eyes with her shirt, she sat quietly for a few moments while staring at the porch floor and then burst into expletive punctuated laughter. Loany threw her hands up into the air and let out a shout. "Dammit, Okie—where in the hell are you? Get out here and hear this story." Turning back toward me she asked, "Did they take her in?"

"Yes, and she's fine. No breaks, no sprains, no blood."

"Her legs were sticking out of the window well..." Loany said it out loud one more time for good measure, and without waiting for a reply smacked a leg and burst out a hearty, "Hell's bells!"

Okie appeared at the front door and stood looking out the screen at us before slowly stepping onto the front porch.

"Hey, bay-bay," he called out his pet name to anyone half a century younger than him.

"Go on and tell him what you just told me," Loany urged. And so I went back through my story, and Loany enjoyed it just as heartily the second time around. Okie, on the other hand, sat looking at me blankly. It just wasn't as funny to a guy about the same age as Scotch Rocks.

"That's what you got me up to hear?" Okie's voice had a hint of annoyance as he looked over at Loany. "I'm going back in and lay down, Loany," he declared.

"You old fart," she chided affectionately. "Where's your sense of humor?" Loany rolled her eyes at me while shaking her head in high drama, but her face held the look of acceptance and understanding that comes with fifty years of loving another.

"You're not working today?" I was surprised to find Loany relaxing porch-side at Paradise Rice, because the fall season was an extremely busy time at Circle S Farms.

"No...today's my day off. Oh, Margie Anne, you *must* come out to the farm. You just won't believe what all we are up to." Loany leaned forward and placed an open palm across her chest. "Yeah-ess, amazing things," she added, her voice taking on the hint of a southern accent Loany effected whenever trying to make the grandest points of import. She did the transition without even noticing, assuming the refined and old Atlanta money-dripping drawl of her aunt Leona and namesake, a woman formally and informally known to all as Big Mamma. Big Mamma resided and held family court in Atlanta's wealthiest of neighborhoods, Buckhead. Loany adored that woman and their two lives were interspersed in a parallel universe of shared similarities that was also punctuated by stark and sometimes crass contradictions in delivery and style.

Big Mamma reigned supreme and all within her reach sought permission from her on every aspect of their lives. Where Loany's social station and control only allowed her to tell people what to do while she had money, Big Mamma would carry her influence and power beyond the death of her wealth-providing husband. Her daughter Dorothy would attend Agnes Scott, the prestigious college and finishing school that strived "to educate women for the betterment of their families and the elevation of the region." Dorothy's arrival into adulthood was announced by a formal cotillion, whereas Loany's schooling ended after eight years and her emergence into the public eye was that of notorious, home-wrecking floozy and law-dodging racketeer. Big Mamma and Dorothy were genteel in voice and smooth in delivery. Loany blasted her obscenities that could be heard half a restaurant away. But in keeping with the mores of Southern hospitality and the bond of family, their visits in either Buckhead or Georgesville lasted for weeks and were the happiest of times. Loany's temporarily acquired Southern accent stuck hard and hung on long after goodbyes had been said. Years after Big Mamma died, Loany still resurrected the drawl inspired by her aunt and called it up as an underscore to certain moments.

Loany reached forward now and pinched my arm for emphasis. "Waah, aah am working every day next week so do come bah. After that it will be faah too busy for me to show you around." With Loany there was never a thought of a request from her being an option, in her head or within the mind of the recipient. And so, I found myself pulling up in front of Circle S Farms a few days later.

The farm market had grown considerably since the mid-seventies when grain and beef farmers Doug and Ethel Sullivan's children first set up a sawhorse table at the road in front of their farmhouse to sell sweet corn. Next came strawberries and red raspberries and soon cantaloupes were added. Doug built a melon stand, and shortly after, he decided they needed a proper building with doors so no one could steal their hard grown produce. About that same time the Sullivan's began studying with a horticulturist, and he got them in the pumpkin business. Having flowers on hand to decorate with and offer to the children that visited the farm seemed like a nice addition, so a large patch of earth was set aside to grow numerous varieties of everlasting—blue salvia and lavender, statice and strawflower. Ethel had always been a baker too, so a kitchen area with industrial-sized ovens and mixing equipment found their way to the back wall of the main market building behind glass display cases to feature her cookies and shortcakes.

I looked around while my eyes adjusted from the sunny outdoors to the dim glow inside. It was just the kind of place that suited Loany. Knickknacks crammed every nook and tabletop. An autumn flower basket, pumpkins, and a large dollhouse lined the top of a tall refrigerator case. Cracker tins, a teakettle, and a ceramic butter jug stood guard on a shelf above them. Ethel's antique stove collection was scattered out across the main floor and set loose borders as a kind of meandering path to guide customers through the market. Her vintage mixers and flour sifters decorated the stovetops, and in every direction I looked, on the tables and shelves, there was a menagerie of functional country cooking, canning, and farm living paraphernalia—an old lunch pail, a watering can, dried flower arrangements, and a maple syrup bucket. A wood trellis littered with hanging baskets covered the ceiling above the gourmet food section that was aisles and aisles of custom-made dried dip and cheese mixes, jams, and pie fillings in every flavor imaginable. I'd never heard of some of the concoctions I discovered mixed with old favorites. I scanned the neatly lettered tub and jar labels—pineapple salsa, horseradish and cranberry cheese spread, pumpkin butter, strawberry salsa, sweet and sassy meat sauce, cheddar cheese ball, cocktail sauce, mango berry salsa.

I wandered around a glass bakery case into the kitchen area that was clearly off-limits to the public, and it suddenly dawned on me the dozens of ladles, whisks, funnels, measuring cups, and wood spoons hanging on pegboard I was staring at were not for sale. I quickly backed out of the kitchen.

"Mar-gay!" I heard Loany's hello bellow before she appeared in my peripheral vision. I turned around to greet her and bumped into an old-time, wood candy bin filled with licorice and dried fruit. Her eyes lit up as she slapped me a hello.

"It's about time you stopped by. There's so much I want you to see," she declared while pushing me out a back door and into a Circle S Farms celebration of the fall harvest and al fresco presentation of all things country. Around me was a display of colors and textures—brown, orange, maroon, and yellow set on a backdrop of green fields glistening with the dew of the morning. Gourds and flower arrangements topped benches and tables; Indian corn hung on the sides of the buildings; and of course, there were pumpkins—tons and tons of pumpkins.

"We want Circle S to be a fun experience for the whole family," Loany explained proudly. "I told Doug and Ethel we have to take care of the children. Come see what we are doing to the barn." Loany set out toward a massive Dutch-styled structure, its gabled roof towering as high as the mighty oaks nearby. Corn shocks circled with pumpkins lined "Fodder Lane," and as we walked she purposely stopped from time to time, acting as an informal tour guide.

"Now you know, we already have a petting zoo for the kids." Loany steered me off the lane toward an animal pen. I didn't really know much of anything about Circle S except that it was where I came to purchase strawberries every spring, but I mumbled and nodded my head in agreement. Black and white pigmy goats lay in a pen contentedly munching on feed. A couple of bunnies peeked out of the pen next to them. Turkeys and ducks roamed free and were charging toward Loany, ever the bird lady.

"Aren't you afraid kids will get hurt with those birds running loose?" My formal risk management training kicked in as I contemplated the liability aspects of this business model.

Loany looked at me with amusement. "Hell no. Those birds won't let the kids catch them." She nudged me into motion again toward the barn.

"What's that for?" I pointed back across the lane toward a brightly painted orange and red antique tractor with a platform of hay surrounding it.

"It's for the kids to play on," Loany looked over at me as if I'd never been the parent I'd never been. "Now over here at the edge of the field is a scarecrow hay bale cave, and of course, there's a cornflower maze, too." We reached the barn and she led me inside. "But, the fun barn is my favorite. The children just love it." Loany stood looking around in the barn, wearing a smile of accomplishment and pride. Terraced mountains climbed toward the barn roof in all directions, a jungle gym of square hay bales with dips and turns to be discovered and conquered. A shiny bright slide returned the explorers back from rafter level to the barn floor to begin their adventure anew.

"Each visitor gets a hay ride and stop to select their very own pumpkin from the patch to take home."

"Where do you take them on the hay ride?" I looked around the flat expanse of fields in every direction.

"Back toward the creek to the pumpkin patch," Loany pointed to a stand of trees far in the distance. She motioned to a driver pulling four wagons and pushed me toward one named the "green bean machine."

"You want to take a ride?" she asked while calling out to the driver.

"Nah, I'll pass today."

"Now everyone gets a donut and cider, and on weekends, we have a food concession and live music, too."

As we walked back toward the farm entrance, Loany babbled on and on, a fire in her eyes and excitement rising and falling in her voice as she thought of more to tell me about Circle S Farms.

"Try one of these donuts. They are so delicious," she exclaimed as she pushed one toward my mouth. I glanced up at a sign on the wall that was hanging below a birdhouse propped on a shelf strung with twinkle lights. "Just Another Day in Paradise." Perfect.

* * *

Loany attacked her career at Circle S like all the others that had come before it—with energy and commitment and passion. She was usually one of the first to arrive every morning, well before seven o'clock, and greeted Ethel who was already busy frying up donuts. Loany set to work sprucing the place up, and as other employees began to trickle in, they knew to be on the lookout for the bleach-soaked mop she flailed around wildly and willfully. Many a blue jean leg bottom had been sacrificed to her purposeful deck swabbing. And her co-workers need not consider spouting negative thoughts or complaining about being tired or some other silly-assed thing within Loany's earshot. She didn't want to hear anything about it and reminded them they were all a good fifty years younger than her. There was work to be done.

There was no farm chore around Circle S Farms Loany didn't embrace and consume, in spite of her age and despite of her skill set, or the complete and utter lack thereof. She was intent and eager to sample all tasks, and early on she set her sights on riding the transplanter. It was an odd looking contraption of a machine with two seats facing backwards to that of the tractor driver, with a hopper in the middle to deposit flower seedlings into the earth.

"You know, Leona, you're getting too old to do that," Doug cautioned.

"By God, I can ride that transplanter if you'll just give me the chance," Loany countered.

But, Doug was not convinced it was such a good idea for a woman of her age. Working on the transplanter was a hot and dirty job. The ride in the fields was a bumpy one, and she could fall and get hurt. Loany, on the other hand, was obsessed about riding the transplanter, and thought it was just about the neatest thing she had never done. Had to do it. Had to do it. Just had to do it. She pestered Doug about it for days, never wavering in her intent to help deliver the five acres of flower seedlings planted every spring at Circle S.

Shortly after their discussion, she arrived at work adorned in her chosen outfit for the mission, a selection with her distinctive flair and functionality that escaped the understanding or rationale of any ordinary person—terry cloth shorts, a bright yellow tube top straining across her chest, and a fluffy hat resembling a shower cap that was covered in yellow flower petals. She claimed her spot on the transplanter and laughed and bounced across the fields, an eighty-year-old Big Bird figure with hefty boobs and a potty mouth.

"You know, I've done every job on this farm but lick the dog's ass," Loany said with satisfaction. And in return, she was not the least bit shy about reaching out and asking for a favor—to be helped out of a jam.

"Listen," Loany directed to Ethel one day. "We have this goose that follows Okie everywhere. Can I bring it here? It's shitting all over the place. It follows Okie and sits on the porch until he comes out. It's just a mess around the house."

Ethel had no problem adding one more fowl to the farm's collection, so Loany lugged the goose to Circle S. Everyone expected him to head toward the pond and check out his new digs and bird buddies, but the water bird hovered around the store and wouldn't leave there. Whenever the door opened, he made a mad dash, lunged inside and waddled over to the cash register and plopped down right next to it.

"I swear he thinks he's human," Loany said shaking her head.

The goose became a regular fixture next to the market checkout, and someone dubbed him Okie Goose. The title seemed fitting to Loany since he shit all over her porch to begin with because he was so in love with Okie.

For well over a decade, she settled into the rhythms of the farm at Circle S. Spring brought the first warm days of the year, planting time, and strawberry season. Loany moved around the grounds visiting with the customers and directing the you-pick-your-own berry hunters.

Summertime meant she would sell Circle S produce at the farmers' market every weekend in Grove City, along the old main street of the city's historical downtown and just a stone's throw away from Beulah Park, the racetrack that had been her and Okie's haunt in an existence decades gone by and money long since gone.

Loany presented the group with special shirts she personally designed of burgundy and beige, the back sporting a circle with a giant "S" in the middle of it. She refused to take any money for them. Doug surveyed her creation and said, "Leona, that looks like a bull's-eye. I can't wear that shirt; people will want to shoot at me. It looks like a big target." It was just so important, she told Doug and Ethel, that they all had matching shirts. It elevated and set them apart from all the other produce growers.

Fall was the busiest of times at Circle S with pumpkin season in full roar. Loany worked the phones nonstop booking hayrides—talking with church pastors, teachers, parents, nursing home administrators—anyone to whom she could sell a hayride and fall farm adventure.

"Leona, you need to back off a bit," Doug cautioned her. "I've only got so many spots in the woods. Don't sell more than we've got."

"I'm gonna sell them, Doug," Loany countered with conviction. "We'll have people who don't show up."

In winter, Loany tagged along with Ethel to gourmet food shows and trade events to market Circle S goods to wholesalers. She commanded an entrance while wandering around making new friends and collecting freebies. Loany worked the booth bearing witness to passersby on the glory of Circle S goods. People assumed she was Ethel's mother—two fast talking, chatty blondes about the same height, standing side by side.

Every winter after the New Year, Loany and Okie hitched a ride down to Florida with Maxine to spend a couple months with transplanted members of the Goldhardt German hillbilly clan. Loany wandered up and down the beach barefoot collecting shells and visited flea markets while Okie fished in a little boat off the local canal. Then the Rices returned home to Georgesville in time for Loany to start the Circle S cycle of the seasons all over again.

If it ever wore on Loany that she was still working a job a good twenty years after most people retired, well, she never mentioned it. She needed the money and something else, I'm sure—a place to belong, and think, be vital, and make a contribution. As the years stacked up at Circle S, Loany was as much a fixture at the farm as the buildings there, and she fussed over the place like it was her very own. Loany put her signature tweak and touches onto all things produce, farm fun and confectionary. Everything had to be just perfect. In pumpkin season, she set the tables just so, with flowers she gathered and arranged. Loany dragged straw bales up to stage, added a scarecrow, gourds, and pumpkins. And more flowers. She stood back and surveyed her creation, then adjusted and readjusted. One more bunch of Indian corn. Too many gourds.

She steered seniors much younger than her on tour around in wheelchairs. Loany beamed when a group of her tickies came over from Park West to visit. "Willie," she boomed out, "sing for me. Sing me the blues, Willie boy."

Many of the patrons just assumed Loany owned Circle S. "By God, I'm not the owner," she countered quickly when someone would stop her and ask.

"Leona, just go on and act like you own it," Ethel encouraged after overhearing such a conversation. "Just go on and do your thing. They'll all leave me alone, and I can go do my work and won't have to answer any questions. You can go visit with them."

Loany assumed the post of Circle S ambassador with the patrons while she watched over the business. She always had ideas, ways to make things prettier, and her business instincts were sharp as ever. Doug came to rely on her as a sounding board.

"So what do you think?" he said one day as he finished up a business pitch to her.

"Well, I think that's a good idea, and I think we ought to do it, Doug." Other times Loany shook her head and said solemnly, "I think that's a bad idea, and it will cost you too much money right now. Can you get the return you need?"

When Circle S came up short on drivers one pumpkin season Loany piped up with a solution. "Okie can drive for you."

"He can?" Doug and Ethel glanced back and forth at each other.

"Why sure," Loany replied. Nothing struck her as odd about a eighty-something-year-old guy driving a massive tractor around the farm, pulling wagons of squealing kids and grinning adults. "He'd love it." And so Okie drove for Circle S Farms, and he did love it. Clad in flannel shirt, hat and twinkle in his eye, he was just an anonymous guy having fun. His station was a far cry from the day when his very presence parted and hushed a crowd.

Doug and Ethel Sullivan came to think of Loany and Okie as family. And not surprisingly, Loany accepted them as such.

"You know, Doug," she told the owner one day, "you don't have a mother, and I don't have a son, so we'll just adopt each other."

* * *

The winter came when Maxine left for Florida without Loany and Okie. She felt they were getting too old to make the drive despite the fact Loany was eighty-five years old and still working full bore roar at Circle S, and not to mention, Okie was even ten years older. Of course Loany didn't agree with any of it, particularly the part about her and Okie getting stuck in Ohio. She called up the airlines and booked two one-way tickets headed south.

"Come pick us up at the airport. We're here," she announced over the phone to a flabbergasted, Maxine. Dammit.

That spring, just like every other when they were deposited back at Paradise Rice, the first thing Okie did was to grab his car keys.

"Come on, Loany. Let's drive out to Circle S and see how the strawberries are doing."

CHAPTER 12

A Summer Outing

"When in the hell are you two going to be finished?"

—Okie Rice

It was always a pleasure to hear from the Franklin County Sheriff, but quite unusual to receive a call from him at work during the business day. James "Big Jim" Karnes was a very different man than those who had worn the badge back during Loany and Okie's numbers racketeering payoff days. Big Jim was as squeaky clean as a bar of soap comes out of the wrapper and honest to a tee, with a sense of integrity and straight-shooting plus earthiness thrown in for good measure. Those character traits won him three virtually uncontested terms and a record as the longest serving sheriff in the county's history. Another distinguishing factor from his predecessors was he happened to be Loany's nephew, and so, also my cousin. When I picked up the phone, he just started talking.

"Leona called me last night." Jim was one of the few who actually referred to Loany by her birth name. "She wanted me to shoot off her fireworks," Big Jim added. "I told her, 'Leona, I cannot shoot off your fireworks. I'm the Franklin County Sheriff for God's sake. Call Margie.'" I smiled at the thought.

I was not surprised at Big Jim's stance. Thinking back over a decade of Fourth of July fireworks bashes held at Aunt Maxine's place, I could not ever recall his presence at them. For a man like Big Jim, life's morés were very clear. Fireworks were against the law, and he was a sheriff sworn to uphold the law. One did not place himself in a compromising situation where illegal activity might occur, no matter how trivial. Period.

For Loany, the extreme ends of the black and white continuum had a mile wide shade of grey smashed squarely in between them. Laws were fine community conventions, but ones to be selectively interpreted and adapted to the moment. Crimes against others were certainly egregious. But gambling and fireworks fun? An activity that didn't hurt anyone just wasn't a real crime in Loany's mind, so what the heck. The game was simply to not get caught.

"I made her promise she wouldn't light them herself. That was the deal we cut when I took her to buy them," I explained to Jim. Amazingly, Loany had gone right along with my conditions, which kind of blew my mind. I wasn't so insensitive as to point out she was in her late eighties now and had no business setting off mortars on her own. It just seemed we were on the same unspoken page anyway.

"I took her and Okie to the outlet south of Lancaster," I continued.

"Oh, I heard all about it," the sheriff chuckled.

"I'll bet the version you heard was a little different from the one rerunning in my head."

"Tell me about it," Big Jim urged.

* * *

I had absolutely balked when I arrived at Paradise Rice and found Okie standing on the front porch, dressed in a three-piece suit, suspenders, a summer top hat and cane in hand, ready for action. It wasn't that I minded having Okie along. I was simply concerned my skill set wasn't adequate to handle them both at eighty-seven and ninety-seven years old, respectively. I should have expected Okie would be in tow. He didn't care much about fireworks, but he did relish getting out of the house. Every time and any time. Particularly when it meant a meal out would be included in the excursion.

Loany bounced out through the front door much more appropriately dressed for the mission and predicted mid-nineties temperatures—terry cloth Capri pants, sleeveless blouse, and tennis shoes. Her ensemble was accessorized by a walking cane, which was a new, unexpected addition, from my perspective.

"Damn thing," Loany grumbled when I pointed at the cane. "I just bring it along to shut everyone up," she added.

Forty-five minutes later, we pulled into the fireworks store parking lot and Loany's eyes lit up when she spied the building. It was in fact, a substantial structure, a virtual "Wally World" of sizzle and pop power. Okie insisted he remain in the car, despite my concern over the heat. Felt fine to him, he maintained. And indeed this was the man who jammed so many Duralogs into his fireplace the indoor temperature at Paradise Rice rarely dipped below eighty during the winter months. Visiting them without wearing a bikini was gruesome.

I began to think maybe this outing was going to be much easier than I originally imagined. With Okie hanging out in the car, I could focus solely on stabilizing Loany. And off she went, eagerly bounding toward the door, already weaving and swaying off balance.

"The cane," I shrieked. "Maybe you should use the cane?" Obviously, my first thought had been right. This was going to be a nightmare afternoon.

"For Christ's sake. I'm fine," Loany shot back with a look of annoyance thrown in. "Damn thing's the problem," she said and firmly gripped my arm.

Okay, I thought. *This will work. I'll be your walking cane if you promise to slow down and act your age, whatever that means.*

Once inside, Loany stopped cold, staring in disbelief. A slow smile spread across her face. There were aisles and aisles of product, stacked high to the ceiling of the warehouse. Where to start? As I began to guide her up and down the aisles of fireworks, a young woman appeared smiling at the sight of a senior citizen beaming like a kid at the circus.

"This is my aunt I told you about. The one who sold the fireworks back in the seventies when it was illegal," I said, hoping this would differentiate me from the thousands of other customers.

"Ah, yes," she replied. "What do you think of our store?" she directed toward Loany.

"It is wonderful. Excellent selection and good prices too. Very fair." Loany looked down at a box of fountains on the shelf. "Now you know, these Black Cats are overrated in my opinion," she offered, expert to expert. "I much prefer the ones Phantom makes."

"Me too," the woman replied. They were becoming fast friends. "Hey, let me show you these cakes over here. They're new." She looked up at me and said, "Listen, I'll stay with your aunt. You go ahead and do your shopping."

"Go on," Loany agreed. "We're fine here." As a rookie buyer, I had been dismissed.

I quickly lost myself in the maze of colors, shapes and packages, reading the back of the boxes to try to figure out what to purchase. *Twelve mortar kit with artistic color design paying tribute to European shell designers....* Hmmm. I wonder what those guys did so special they get their own tribute. I grabbed another box from a shelf. *Six special select shells for really unique effects including crackling stars, strobing stars and dragon tail....* Okay, that sounds pretty good. *Five hundred grams of green glitter, gold crackle flying fish and falling leaf effects with beautiful brocade finale.*

The tug on my shirt some time later startled me. I turned as the voice of a young woman said, "Ma'am, your uncle. I believe the gentleman is your uncle."

"Crap. Okie." I had forgotten all about him sitting in the baking oven of my car. I glanced at my watch as I bounded toward the front of the store. He'd been out there almost thirty minutes. Good God. Adult Protective Services would surely cart me away.

"He's fine now," the store clerk assured me, following behind, close on my heels. "I helped him inside and gave him some water. It's very hot outside you know," she added with a tone of judgment and condemnation.

As I rushed toward the front of the store, I spied Okie, sitting with his legs crossed on a wooden folding chair, powdered blue suit and white summer dress hat flawlessly positioned. His posture was perfect. One hand was draped across his knee with the bottled water dangling down from it. The other was anchored on top of his cane, and he looked more like a star posing on a movie set than an almost one hundred-year-old guy I nearly killed. Okie looked past me, his gaze dignified and regal, or was that pissed off?

"When in the hell are you two going to be finished?" His voice was calm, but insistent.

"Are you okay?" I asked, not answering his question. I still had the guilt of a geezer beater hanging over me.

"I'm fine," Okie replied in a tone that suggested he was not the problem. It was Loany and me. "I'm hungry. When are we going to go eat?"

I hurried to collect the discarded fireworks that were scattered on the floor where I'd left them and met Loany at the checkout. She glanced at my pile of goodies as the clerk rang up my order.

"You do want the Black Cats on those," she noted, pointing toward my pile. The clerk nodded in agreement and a substitution was quickly fetched. We both grinned at each other when our shopping totals nearly mirrored each other at one hundred fifty dollars each. Loany's cash came out of the customary cleavage locker, while I began to fill out the required disclaimer.

"What's that?" she asked, pointing at the slip.

"This is the paper we have to sign that says where we are taking the fireworks out of state," I explained.

"Hell's bells," Loany was shaking her head. "I'm not taking mine out of state. Hell no, I'm going to let them off right in my backyard."

"Sure you are taking them out of state." I shot her a stern look. Fudging the facts was not a part of Loany's personality profile, and she offered up the package of her person raw and totally unedited. Truth was an absolute and unspoken agreement to treat others as she would like to be treated.

"That's right," the sales clerk joined in. "You know it's illegal to shoot off fireworks in Ohio."

"So where are you taking yours?" Loany smirked. She was enjoying playing with me now, but clearly had no intention of playing the Ohio fireworks game.

"I take them to my cousin Joan's every Labor Day in Kalamazoo. The one who lives on the lake…"

"Right."

Well, okay, as selective presentation went, I usually had the good intention of taking one or two items with me. Come on, Loany. Get with it.

"You can't tell me the cops buy this?" She held up the affidavit form.

"I have no idea what they buy." I was losing patience with the game now. "Just fill out the form so we can get Okie to a restaurant."

"Okay, I guess I'll take mine to Kalamazoo, too," she muttered.

* * *

Okie's outlook improved dramatically since food was the next agenda item. I scanned the roadside, searching for a family style, diner-type restaurant I'd passed hundreds of times over the years I had spent en route between Ohio University and home. I couldn't remember the name, but it seemed like just the type of place Okie and Loany would love. Breakfast was served all day long, and there was pot roast and chops on the menu alongside burgers, homemade soup, chopped sirloin, catfish fillet, and pasta. This was a basic Americana turn of the century put some meat-on-your-ribs and fat-on-your-ass restaurant.

As I pulled into the parking lot, Loany piped up. "I haven't been here for years. This is just fine," she reassured me.

What wasn't fine were the four steep concrete steps without a railing I spotted that separated us from a cozy seat inside of the diner. How was Okie going to get up them? Luckily at the pace he moved, I had plenty of time to think about my predicament. Unlike Loany, who jerked around in fits and starts, Okie did a great Tim Conway impersonation, taking baby steps inches at a time, head bent down watching his feet, cane firmly posted at his side. He didn't want any assistance and brushed off attempts to steady him, regardless of how dangerous the terrain.

Maybe I could get Loany inside quickly and return before Okie hit the steps. But, Loany was going nowhere because the two of them were arguing over what year the handsome old Cadillac was in the parking lot, and discussing what years and colors they had owned.

"I'm telling you, Okie, that's a fifty-nine. Look at the fins. It's obvious." I had to agree with her. With limited knowledge of vintage cars even I knew there was a dramatic change in the tail fins in 1960.

"I know it's not a sixty," Okie snapped back. "It's a fifty-seven, just like the green one I had."

"You didn't have a green one. It was aqua."

"For Christ's sake, I think I know the cars I owned."

"You mean Thelma and Louise green?" I offered up in an attempt to end the debate. They both stopped and looked over at me, and ignored my remark. My comment obviously meant nothing to them, and the movement of my mouth was clearly an aggravation.

As the quarrel continued, we inched across the parking lot, a cluster of canes and cursing with me bobbing around uselessly, hovering near the pair. I walked backwards in front of them a few paces, and then bolted to the rear. I raised my hands out toward them and dropped them back to my side. I looked like a total idiot.

"What in the *hell* are you doing?" Loany demanded. I had absolutely no idea.

As we reached the bottom step, one of the glass double doors popped open, and a pale, round-faced man with thinning silver hair smiled down at us. He descended down the steps and extended a hand toward Okie, who immediately slapped it away.

"I'm ninety-seven you know," Okie declared, in testimony of what, I wasn't exactly sure. With four of us trying to negotiate the same step, I wedged my body sideways through the group and bolted on up the stairs to open the second glass door. Maybe Okie and Loany could use the doors as a handrail? Or bounce off of them on the way to the pavement and a split skull or broken hip? I dissociated the entire remaining journey to the threshold of the restaurant.

When we finally reached the lobby, a waitress ushered us to a table, and Loany quickly took the seat that gave her a *primo* view of the main dining room, the entryway, and into a second seating area beyond. Okie was content to stare at the wall, while I faced the kitchen.

"Is that all you're going to eat?" Okie asked as the waitress plopped a BLT down in front of me. He settled in over a plate stacked full of liver and onions and began to methodically cut the meat into tidy, bite size pieces.

No way will he finish all that, I thought to myself.

Loany helped us both along with our meals by reaching over unannounced and uninvited to pick food from our plates with her fork.

"You've got your own food, dammit," Okie declared, pointing over at her chicken dish.

"I know. I just want to see if yours is any good."

I finished my sandwich as Okie completed cutting up his meat and arranging the plate to his satisfaction. Liver and onions were positioned precisely at six o'clock, mashed potatoes at about ten-thirty, and some sort of cooked greens thing hovering near two o'clock. My typical lunchtime in corporate America was spent wolfing down junk food while answering emails or balancing my checkbook—a far departure from Okie's near centurion pace of life. I headed to the restroom and returned to find he had made it through about three bites. I checked my watch. I'd left my house at eight that morning and we were well over five hours into what I had thought would be a three-hour jaunt. I found myself edgy and impatient, ready to hit the road, and move on with it.

Loany, however, was quite content with our station in the day. She filled the time striking up a conversation with strangers at the next table and people watching.

"Oh, I had a suit just like that," she said, pointing at a woman across the room. "It was fine. Very rich. Got it at the Union. Paid a good price for it, too."

Then she spied the known entities—a man and woman were smiling and approaching our table. I had no idea who they were, but I wasn't surprised. Loany had a way of running into people sixty or six hundred miles from home. I absolutely knew what was coming next, and the only thing to do was feign mastery at her connectivity lesson.

"Oh, yes. Dad talks about Otto all the time," I replied to Loany earnestly. Otto? I think he was my great grandfather's brother? Wait. Maybe he was my grandfather's brother. And these people were Otto's what? "I'll be sure to tell Mom and Dad I ran into you," I said in my most serious and sincere tone.

"I'm going to the bathroom," Okie declared, as he grabbed his cane. Half his plate of food was gone, and so surely he must have been finished with lunch. I expected him to take some time getting to and fro, but after ten minutes I was becoming a bit concerned.

"Is Okie okay?" I asked Loany. "He's been gone quite awhile."

"He's fine," she assured me. She was busy eavesdropping on a conversation close by.

But, I wasn't so sure. I glanced toward the entryway and watched the men's room door. No one was going in or coming out either. I could imagine Okie had lots of armor to negotiate; suspenders, belt, zipper, suit jacket, and cane. That would take a ninety-seven-year-old some time. Still... Over ten minutes? Oh my God, what if he was sick? I knew little of his day-to-day medical regimen. Okie had to be taking some sort of medication, probably lots of different pills. My mind began to race with bad scenarios. What if he had fallen and was lying on the floor with his head split open? Then, it hit me; oh my God, what if he had died in there? On my watch. What in the hell was I thinking to take these two on solo? Okie had gotten away from my cousin's husband one morning out at breakfast and had fallen pretty hard. And Keith was a well-seasoned attendant, a big burly, strong guy who could have bench pressed Okie with one hand.

I nudged Loany. "He's fine. Just forget about it," she barked at my anxiousness. As I was scooting my chair back to make a run on the boy's room, a man appeared at the door and walked in. Whew. Okay. Patience. I barely breathed and did not take my eyes off the men's room door while a couple more minutes slowly ticked off the game clock.

When the restroom door popped back open, my man scout appeared, relaxed in his own life and world as he crossed the dining room to rejoin his party. There certainly appeared to be no emergency in at the urinals. I glanced at my watch for the hundredth time. We were now approaching fourteen minutes. The next time the door opened, it was Okie. Seventeen minutes.

He settled back in at the table and hunkered down over his plate to continue assaulting the liver and onions. Dang, he had a sound appetite, an amazing appetite, in fact, for a very old guy.

"Why I'll try some of that coconut cream pie I saw you carry out," Loany replied to our waitress' offer for dessert.

"What else you got?" Okie asked.

* * *

Loany let Big Jim the sheriff off the hook and offered her stash to me, and with both our fireworks at my disposal this was going to be the best show ever. No doubt about it. Every year I put on my little display for an assortment of relatives who housed over after mom's family reunion. At seventy-five yards wide open to the centerline of the roadway, my parents' country home was a great pyrotechnics theater. I set up a launch pad in the middle of the gravel driveway fifty yards out from the paver walkway filled with lawn chairs and DEET-covered observers. Loany and Okie had VIP seating up front.

I surveyed the boxes of booty and began staging it in piles by type a ways from the launch site. I figured I could get about fifteen minutes of pretty continuous firepower, all mixed up with some nice variety. I had six mortar tubes on hand and lined them up on a long piece of plywood. Each cannon would get at least a minute to cool down between blows.

I called on a friend to help me with the discharge duties, and we devised a plan to shoot off two mortars simultaneously. I signaled the crowd and we began the detonation dance. "Three, two, one," I counted out as we both attempted to light fuses in unison at the zero mark and then bolt back several yards to clear away from the launch tubes. Sometimes our method worked, and sometimes it didn't. But every time, we most certainly looked a little loony, for sure. This year's group was not a particularly easy crowd. Over the years, the exhibition expectations rose along with the age of my kin.

"Bor-ing. Can't you go any faster?" I heard my seven-year-old cousin's voice above the crowd chatter.

You know what, Andrew? I would love to go faster, but the breeze is blowing the lighters out, and when it's not doing that, I'm burning my thumb, you little smartass. I smiled and waved to him but said nothing. With technical difficulties delaying the show, it was now far beyond dusk, and I strained my eyes in the twilight to locate the mortar fuse. A flashlight would have been a nice touch. I was suddenly not having much fun. At all.

"Here—go set off this cube to shut everyone up," I urged, pointing toward a pile of fireworks. Beyond my outstretched finger a spark of light behind the crowd caught my attention, a glowing fire bobbing gently back and forth in the night sky. It was moving toward me, but I couldn't see what it was, until my father's figure came into focus as he slowly and methodically walked toward us with a lit blow torch in his hand.

"Here, this should work," he declared.

"Okay, let's do a couple white ones," I directed. We hurried to load two mortar shells for Dad to light simultaneously. "I so love the sperm-toids," I squealed, as I liked to call them, their soft white octopus tentacles drifting down slowly to the earth against the horizon.

With three of us shooting off mortars, the crowd settled down. I could hear applause from time to time. Laughter. Oohs and aaaahs. The show was advancing nicely now, moving forward so quickly, in fact, I would surely be out of pop power in about five more minutes. My annoyance meter had ratcheted back down to zero, and I caught myself having fun and enjoying the moment. This was much better. Life as it should be.

"Okay, now we'll do a fountain and let the tubes cool off. Grab some Roman candles and we'll get them going, too."

I surveyed my last pile of mortars. I was saving one very special big boy that had seven different mortar blasts in it for the end.

"Here's the last regular mortar before we start the grand finale."

I had drifted a couple steps backward when the bang hit us all at chest level, about three feet above the launch tube. Shards of light and fire were flying everywhere and seemed to pass right through my body. I froze. My hands and fingers tingled in an innate surge of flight or fight programmed DNA. My instincts were way ahead of my brain that was still struggling to make sense of the data my eyes sent it. My two assistants had not moved or spoken either. Somehow, none of us had been touched by the blast. Had I been able to see it, I am confident my dad's face would have been ashen. His hand was still outstretched and holding the blow torch. He said nothing.

The misfire had startled the peanut gallery into dead silence, too. It was as if time froze and stood still, though probably in reality only a few seconds had passed on life's clock.

Loany's strong, familiar voice rang out in the quiet of the night. "Good one, Marg!"

CHAPTER 13

Christmas Eve's Eve

"It's my very favorite of them all."
                                    —Loany

I always found myself a bit out of sorts on December twenty-third. School was out, and the nonstop chaos from holiday festivities earlier in the month had subsided. All the shopping was done too, and the gifts were wrapped, so there wasn't much to do but pass time in wait for the main events. Pat and I rode around in his stepfather's yellow Buick convertible, bored.

"I know," he exclaimed. "We can go visit Loany. Maybe we can help her out."

This was the one night of the year we could be absolutely certain she would be at home. No doubt about it. For on December twenty-third, Loany would be deep in preparation for her annual Christmas Eve dinner. She had been holding the event for decades, a Loany-fied extravaganza that brought together the Rices and the

Goldhardts, their kids, grandkids and great grandkids; some old and new friends; along with neighbors, friends of friends, and usually a couple people none of us could identify.

Her ritual started in the fifties during the fabulous mega rich years. As a child, the food feast meant little to me, and the part I dreamed about in breathless anticipation was for the magic wonder world Loany transformed Paradise Rice into. Had I been an adult, I might have chosen a word like "opulent" as an overriding label to describe the scene to outsiders. But, as a kid, it was purely a joy to be sampled in serial fashion, wandering from display to display, the sounds and images filling my mind until no more would fit, and I had to let go of one marvel to make room for the next spectacle before my eyes.

There were full-sized decorated Christmas trees in every room, including one with a train running round and round at the bottom of it. Silver trees, white trees, traditional pine trees, and yes, Loany's signature tree, were all crammed into nearly every square inch of Paradise Rice. The inside of the front door was covered with a giant stuffed stocking that sang a Christmas carol whenever a guest entered. Bubble lights were strung on the wrought iron, flowered divider that separated the kitchen from the serving area. Poinsettias sat wherever there were a couple inches of room, and flower arrangements with candles in glass globes made their way to the tables. The windowsills were stuffed full of angel hair and bobbled with lights and electric candles. The bathroom and toilet were adorned too, along with the front porch, ceramic donkey, and bushes outside—though the magnificent decorating event was dedicated to the indoors.

Loany didn't bother to put away all of her everyday knickknacks to make room for Christmas. She just jammed oodles of holiday hoopla in with the rest of her possessions. Shiny bulbs hung suspended on ribbons inside the china hutch and a lighted garland was draped across the top and sides. The mantel disappeared beneath cotton snow, a yuletide village, a glitter of lights. There were snowmen and reindeer, elves and Santas, tucked here and there; some of which were lit up and animated. At Christmastime, Paradise Rice was a medley of small and dimly lit everyday seating vignettes offset by bold, bright, and brassy holiday displays that moved, sang, and filled their assigned spaces. These sentries proclaimed the wonder of Christmas, while the birth of Christ took a bit of a back seat to Santa and his elves.

Loany merged massive, boisterous, and dazzling effortlessly with tiny, modest, and serene. It took several passes through Paradise Rice to notice the more subtle decorating nuances she created—a brass duck lamp with a Santa hat plopped onto its head, or a lone Styrofoam snowman with button eyes and felt scarf, standing guard by the phone.

Loany could have charged admission back then, because Christmastime at Paradise Rice was a spectacular place that, outside of big fancy department stores like Macy's in New York, simply did not exist for ordinary people. Why, we'd heard Santa's sleigh bells outside when he flew over the roof a couple of times, and once Loany even got him to stop at Paradise Rice on his way delivering toys. He stopped and visited with us on his busiest night of the year. Loany actually knew Santa Claus!

It wasn't out of the realm of possibility to imagine Loany *was* Mrs. Claus, because along with the excessive holiday decorating, she relished in purchasing a special gift for every man, woman, and child that joined her on Christmas Eve. These gifts were not common or mass-purchased goods to dole out. Thoughtful reflection about the recipient through the unique eye of Loany often resulted in extraordinary and quite memorable acquisitions.

One Christmas Eve when I was a child, she took my hand and led me into her back bedroom, which was bathed in dim light from a small lamp reflecting off the glass top of an antique beige dresser it sat on. Its warm glow extended out into the dark room around it—intensely bright at the center, it diffused into softer shadows encompassing the golden hues of the dresser. The tiny glow disappeared into the room, a warm beacon that tamed the darkness beyond it.

The light from the lamp was my safe place, and my eyes traced along with it into the black night and rest of the room. I could make out the faint outline of a row of boxes stacked ceiling high on the far wall, stuffed in between the bed and Loany's closet. She maneuvered in the darkness like a cat, steady and sure, sidestepping slippers on the floor. As Loany made her way around to the stack, she stood lost in thought and scanned the pile for a moment.

"Here it is. I picked this out especially for you." She moved quickly back around to me and kneeled down on one knee. Looking at me eye to eye she placed a black square looking box into my hands. "It's a camera...it's called an Instamatic, and look, it has a flash, too!" Loany slipped the strap around my neck. "Somewhere I have batteries and film for this." She laughed and disappeared back into the bright fluorescent light of the kitchen to rummage through drawers.

I wore the camera around all evening, the thing protruding from my seven-year-old washboard chest like an organ grinder without his monkey. Loany planted a seed in a child's mind that night that has endured a lifetime—from first being a casual photo snapper, to becoming the yearbook photographer, to receiving a 35MM Single Lens Reflex camera for high school graduation, and finally, to dreaming of being a photojournalist.

There were some years where theme gifts made their way into her gift bag, particularly for the boys running around Paradise Rice who happened to be about the same age. Battery-operated choo-choo trains puffed smoke as they wobbled across the carpet and fell over. One particular year, I silently envied the boys for being boys, as Loany gathered them around her and presented each with a Mattel "shootin' shell" Remington buckle gun. Attached to a leather belt was a rectangular silver metal buckle tooled with leaves and a large shiny bullet that held a derringer revolver locked in the center of it. Whenever the wearer puffed out his belly, the pistol snapped out on a hinge and shot an authentic looking brass case with a plastic bullet in the end of it. The gun could be unlatched from the buckle whenever a cowboy was in serious trouble, but the secret no-hands firing made it about the neatest thing ever!

On this Christmas Eve's Eve, years after I'd received my camera, Loany was undeniably hard at work in the kitchen and didn't pass up the occasion to direct four extra feet and hands.

"Go downstairs, son and bring up the leaves for the dining room table," she said to Pat. "Oh, and bring up the card tables, too. After that, I'll need the roaster up here for the turkey. Margie, you know where the fruit salad bowl is. Go help Patrick." I had never stopped to consider all that went into this meal I'd come to take quite for granted.

There sure was plenty to do, and an hour later we had run up and down her steep, breakneck stairs dozens of times.

"Here's a Tom and Jerry," Loany announced as she shoved a mug in my hand.

"What's in it?" I asked suspiciously.

"Just drink it—it's good," Loany bellowed back. I brought the cup to my lips and tasted the nastiest, warm, foamy gunk in a thick cream.

"What is in this?" I asked again. "It's awful."

Loany scrunched up her face in disbelief. "My homemade eggnog, brandy, and rum. I do so love them at this time of year. Why, it wouldn't be Christmas without a good Tom and Jerry." She took somewhere between a gulp and outright chug and turned around toward the counter to make herself another one. I set mine aside and motioned to Pat that it was all right for him to do the same.

"What else do you need?" Maybe if I changed the subject Loany would forget about the whereabouts of my mug.

"You can cut up some cheese," Loany motioned toward the refrigerator. "Here are a couple of knives. Make those cubes smaller," she exclaimed, as she watched us begin. "You know there will be one hundred people here tomorrow night I have to feed."

The head count was not an exaggeration, during the fifties or even five decades later. The composition of the crowd changed over time, but certainly not the head count. As Okie's kids grew up and multiplied, they replaced the Rices' gambling friends who had all but drifted away after the money dried up. Okie's kids would have kids who, in turn, grew up, married (or not) and had more kids. Loany's side of the family all did our part to be a well-stocked rail car on the prolific family train, too. And once again, the tarmac, roadways, and yard around Paradise Rice were jammed with automobiles, moving in and out all evening long—the comings and goings requiring a constant dance of musical parked cars, as the unluckiest of us had to run outside countless times to move and then park our car again.

As I entered adulthood, I counted on Christmas Eve at Loany's being the best meal of the year, and I fasted all day in preparation. Both ham and turkey were featured, along with two kinds of dressing—oyster and sage, creamed corn, mounds of mashed potatoes, gravy and homemade noodles my parents had rolled out and dried on every horizontal surface in our house—beds, counters, table tops—most anywhere a dishtowel could hold a batch. Loany served her renowned German coleslaw—shredded cabbage topped with a concoction of whipping cream, vinegar, salt and sugar that pleasantly bit and sweetened the taste buds simultaneously. There were cheese and vegetable trays, crackers, dips, and deviled eggs. Fresh fruit salad was served for dessert. As Pat and I finished up that first Christmas Eve's Eve as assistants, it was nearing midnight.

"I sure do appreciate your kids help," Loany confided, as we put on our coats to leave. While I buttoned up and prepared for the cold night air, I found myself mentally contemplating her age. I had never really considered Loany's age, and I hadn't assigned her a number. Loany didn't conjure up labels; she was just Loany, divine and ageless, the woman who refused to grow old. As I did the math in my mind, I decided she must have been somewhere in her early sixties since I was eighteen. The woman sure had stockpiles of energy.

***

From that first almost accidental intervention, Loany's elves grew into a core collection of half a dozen or so nieces, nephews, and grandkids. Christmas Eve's Eve became the party of the season for our intimate group. The magic was supplied by Loany, and the magic was strong. The enchantment was so intoxicating, in fact, that as the years went by and our lives became more complicated, we all juggled flight schedules—Atlanta, Boston, Denver, and Rochester; the weather; the demands of our careers, and children to make sure we all were in Georgesville, Ohio, at Paradise Rice, whatever may come, by Christmas Eve's Eve.

Marty stood guard directing and guiding the process, because none of us really ever got very good at cooking or food preparation. But, none of that ever bothered Loany one bit. Where she could have easily grabbed a knife from one of us and peeled that pear we were struggling with in half the time, she was content to orchestrate the show and shove Tom and Jerrys at us.

"Good timing, Marg," Marty called out to me as I walked into the kitchen. "We just finished the fruit salad without you."

"Hey, I got here as soon as I could after work. You all could have waited. It's not even seven o'clock yet." No one answered me, and I looked at the group standing around the kitchen table. They all had an odd demeanor, each in a different way. Marty was staring down at the table, biting the edge of her lip as if to suppress a grin. Her daughter Nora wore a very solemn expression, while son Jimmy didn't try to hide the big smile he was sporting. My brother Bill and Nora's husband Keith were crouched over the small sink peeling potatoes. Keith glanced over his shoulder at me, shook his head, rolled his eyes, and turned back to the spuds. Loany slowly stirred the fruit salad with a serving spoon, and stared purposefully into the bowl.

"Grandma can't find one of her fake fingernails," Nora blurted out. The rest of the elves cracked up. Loany shrugged and rolled her eyes.

"Is it in the fruit salad?" I had to ask.

"Well, shit. I've swept the floor and looked everywhere else around here. Haven't we? Jesus Christ." Loany disappeared a moment and returned with a bottle of brandy and poured it into the bowl of fruit. Spiking dessert was always her finishing touch. Made it taste much better, according to her.

"You kids just keep this to yourself," Loany commanded. "It will be our little secret."

"I don't think I'll be eating any this year," Jim announced.

"Keith, Billy. How many pounds of potatoes did we do last year?" Loany had moved on. "Did you see people last year...why, we ran out of about everything. They were scraping the bottom of the bowl."

"I tell you every year it should be at least fifteen pounds," I answered. Though there were lots of small children these days, I could certainly eat a pound of Loany's heavy cream-laced mashed potatoes myself. And invariably, the year after a potato shortage, Loany would end up with tons of potatoes left over. Her elves never got it quite right, despite a group toting roughly a dozen college degrees between us and fancy corporate jobs. The appropriate spud poundage remained an absolute and utter mystery.

On Christmas Eve proper, the elves turned the kitchen over to a much more skilled crew of two—my dad, a man who must have been a short order cook in a previous life the way he relished the mission of feeding the masses; and granddaughter Pam, a real-life skilled event planner and executor. The two moved around like synchronized dancers, arranging the food and refilling serving bowls.

"Excuse me," Pam motioned to those in the food line, "Ron is coming through with more mashed potatoes. Move, move, please."

The electrical demands to power Christmastime at Paradise Rice strained the upper limits of the system, one without breakers but with old fashioned fuses that blew with regularity. The partial blackouts were expected, and would have been a disappointment, in some way, had we made it a year without intermittent darkness.

Loany's voice and laughter boomed out from the darkness. "Jesus Christ, Ronny, we blew another fuse."

"Yeah, Ron must have turned the mixer on to mash more potatoes," Big Jim the sherriff called out to a group of laughing revelers.

By dusk, Paradise Rice was crowded with bodies. The house was nearly full to capacity with a line weaving back out of the serving room through the kitchen and into the living room, neatly blocking the front door and preventing more guests from squeezing inside. Limited table space in the dining room stopped forward movement and progress at times. The food line stalled out and went nowhere. Those in wait stood around chatting with the luck of the draw beside them. "So good to see you," and "I always know I'll get to visit with you on Christmas Eve. How've you been?" Kids pushed their way through the adults standing around, to move from one room to the other. Guests grabbed an open spot on one of the long winding divans bordering the walls in the seating room overlooking the Darbys, and held their dinner plates out in front of them.

A cousin stood over his plate set upon the marble-topped French provincial chest, his body crowding the portrait of Butsy and Loany hanging on the wall next to it. "It was the only place I could find to stand," he shrugged. Paradise Rice was, in fact, an absolute cluster.

After dinner, seating was limited too, and the initiated arrived early, ate, and found a spot to pop a squat, and dared not leave it. Bill Rice played his guitar and took requests in the back seating room. "The Ballad of Okie and Leona" was always a part of his repertoire.

The gift giving had flip flopped to Loany and Okie with a pile surrounding them in the living room, and guests crammed around to watch the opening ritual. Loany ripped through her packages in a few minutes. Cash went right into the cleavage locker, kisses and hugs, oohs and aahs to the hard booty. Okie, on the other hand, was much more methodical and systematic in his gift opening. Retrieving a pocket knife from his trouser pocket, he slowly opened the blade, aligned it sideways and ran it down the seam edge of the gift paper. Next, Okie rotated the package and put the knife into the top of one end. Searching for the tape, he neatly carved a slit, leaving the wrapping paper intact.

Loany looked over and barked, "For Christ's sake Okie, we're not saving that paper. Hurry up!" Okie frowned at her, and then dismissed the order, and went back to aligning the pocket knife on another edge of the package. Satisfied that all the tape had been slit, he closed the blade and slipped the knife back into his suit trousers. "Dammit…haven't you opened one gift yet?"

Okie stacked the cases of Duraflame fire logs he received up in the corner by the hearth and eyed them like his prize race horses, keeping a tally and grinning. The temperature at Paradise Rice would not be dipping below eighty degrees before spring!

Most years I ended up seated near the other elves. The Christmas Eve's Eve crew stuck close together.

"You know, Grandpa is getting up there. How many more years will we all be together at Christmas?" Nora wondered aloud scanning the group, eyes locking last with her brother Jim.

"I know. I've been thinking about that, too," I replied. For the next decade, we revisited the same conversation every Christmas Eve as we watched Loany and Okie open their gifts.

"This has got to be that last year," Jim announced when Okie was in his late nineties.

"Yup. We said that last year, too," Keith chimed in. We all chuckled.

"How old is he now? Is it ninety-six?" I asked.

"Ninety-seven," Nora and Jim replied in unison.

"I sure hope he makes it to one hundred," I confessed. "He so wants to make it to one hundred."

"You know...he could end up outliving Leona," Keith suggested. Loany was no spring chicken herself, edging closer to ninety. The group fell quiet, as each of us undoubtedly put our minds to work rectifying the inevitable in our own way.

Nora was the first to speak. "I've been doing this my entire life. I have never spent one Christmas at home. We've traveled here every year since I was born. My daughter has never spent one Christmas in her own home. It's what we do...it's what we want to do." Jim nodded in agreement.

Loany's Christmas Eve was what we'd all done for so long our minds couldn't contemplate any plausible alternative. As I turned to watch her now, I gazed toward the front door where she sat on the floor, legs tucked to her side, always barefoot and perpetually laughing, the center of the star. I'd seen Loany sit that way and in that very place countless times before, over dozens of years. I could trace a thousand memories of her to that place, to this place I called Paradise Rice, and to a collage of places in my mind where we had been together. All were special, because Loany made paradise wherever she was.

* * *

The summer day was like countless others I aimlessly piddled away while a child as I ran up the walkway toward the front door of Paradise Rice. The sun was piercing and bright, but the blue and white striped porch awning shielded it from blurring my view through the storm door and into the living room. Loany stood within sight just beyond the glass, intently scribbling on a list and looking around the room. As the heavy door banged loudly shut behind me, I found myself surrounded by more fireworks than I'd ever seen in one place. Loany usually kept her stock well hidden, tucked out of sight for safekeeping in the boat house, but these fireworks were apparently destined for a trip up Alkire Road to Goldhardt's Grocery.

I looked around and slowly took in the sight before me. There were cases of bottle rockets, not the two or three packages of a dozen I managed to scrape enough cash together to buy at one time. Boxes of Roman candles were stacked on the hearth, and bricks of various brands of firecrackers sat on the floor blocking the kitchen entryway. I discovered a few packages of mortars, and of course, plenty of sparklers and smoke bombs. I spied an octagonal flat yellow and red wafer looking thing about an inch thick and six inches wide. I'd never seen anything like it before.

"What's this?" I asked, holding it up for Loany to see. "Happy Lamp?" I added, reading the top label.

She looked away from her list. "It's my very favorite of them all . . . it's a Chinese lantern." Loany took it from my hand and pushed me toward the door. "Come on."

She tied the string that was stapled to the top of the wafer to the frame of the porch awning and began digging through her pockets to find some matches. The wafer floated like a Frisbee suspended in midair, gently bobbing back and forth in the breeze. After countless matches failed Loany finally made contact with the fuse, and the wafer jolted into motion. It began to spin wildly on the string, jumping up and down a bit. Rockets buried in the sidewalls of each corner of the wafer spewed out a stream of fire and light and pushed its spinning orbit faster and faster. I moved back quickly and pressed up against the house. If that thing let go, it could certainly take a head off. The rocket boosters had stopped and the wafer was still spinning, but noticeably slower. So far I wasn't incredibly impressed. *Is that all this thing does?* I thought. *What's the big deal?* Then, when it had almost completely stopped spinning with the sound of a gentle poof, the bottom dropped open to reveal pale red and yellow silk streamer sidewalls, and shades adorned in intricate Chinese symbols and figures. Twinkle lights glittered and ricocheted around the inside of the lantern as its spinning began to slow. A giant kite's tail hung from the bottom and acted as an anchor. As the twinkle lights burned out the lantern rested still in its magnificent glory. Loany stood examining it with a huge smile beaming across her face.

"Here, you can have it," she said.

"Really?"

"Sure."

I gingerly took the lantern from Loany and wrapped the string around my hand. Somehow I peddled my bike home one handed without dropping the Chinese lantern and hung it in my bedroom.

* * *

I've thought a lot over the years about why the Chinese lantern was Loany's favorite. Maybe it was because it's the only firework that leaves something behind. All the others simply capture the essence of the celebration at hand.

Maybe it was because a Chinese lantern is something you can keep and treasure, allowing you to look back and remember the amazing swirling light and fire it created.

Maybe it was because a Chinese lantern bursts into being as a freight train of speed and light swirling round and round, a powerful firestorm of momentum.

Maybe it was because, like a Chinese lantern, Loany was never afraid to hang her life from a tiny thread and see the beauty of what this world can offer.

Maybe it was because, like a Chinese lantern, Loany knew the only way to carry on in this world free and unencumbered was to put oneself out on that tiny thread.

Maybe it was because Loany understood the best way to enjoy a Chinese lantern, as in life, was not to be constrained by the burdens you bear. Or else one would never light that match and start the firestorm. Loany was willing to take a risk and light that match.

Early in her life when Loany's Chinese lantern began spinning, it built great speed and momentum until almost spiraling out of control. And, in that moment when everything in life changed as she knew it, and her Chinese lantern slowed and nearly came to a stop, it was quietly building the energy to come back to life and open, to reveal the true beauty within her and allow the realization of all Loany could become—granny to the tickies, country store keep, a migrant farmer, queen of the fish fry.

Her final glow was the culmination of that chance to stop and reflect back on where she'd come from and consider what she really wanted, what really mattered in a life. Her rebirth was that of a phoenix rising up from the ashes; except unlike a phoenix, she never let her tiny fire go completely out.

The freedom of how to live so nobly came from how Loany hung her Chinese lantern on that tiny thread. She was willing to take risks and expose herself—to get on a plane in her eighties and go to Europe, to run from the law and throw numbers slips out of the window of her car, to purchase a one-way ticket to Florida, to overcome and reconcile the most irreconcilable—an only son's death.

Or maybe, just maybe, in the final analysis, Loany loved Chinese lanterns simply because they were, like her, such an exceptional thing of beauty in a class of so many "all-you-others."

For those of us who were lucky enough to have known Loany, her Chinese lantern burns so fierce and bright in our hearts and minds—for now and for always.

As I sit on the hillside somewhere near the spot where eighteen slot machines remain buried far below, I look over my shoulder up at the fading facade of Paradise Rice. It is warm and familiar and comforting. I think I'll stay awhile.

EPILOGUE

I was roughly halfway through this book project when
the Metro Park guys tore down Paradise Rice. I'd been
hearing word that might happen, but I didn't want to think
about it. From time to time, I ran into park rangers while
wandering the farm fields around Georgesville hunting
arrowheads, my hobby and stress reliever to combat twenty-
five years of "boots on the ground" in corporate America.
Those same farm fields I'd passed hundreds of times as a
kid on my way down to Goldhardt's Grocery were now all
park land, having been gobbled up along with Loany and
Okie's place. The park rangers never ran me off the land,
even though the *No Trespassing* signs were large and well
posted—once I threw out that I was Loany and Okie's
niece, anyway. Everyone knew the Rices, and everyone
had their favorite story.

I always asked if they had any idea what was going to
happen to Paradise Rice. It would make a great park office,
I'd remind them, with all that knotty pine wood inside and
a nice lower level garage to park their patrol truck. Why,
one of them could live upstairs in it, I'd offer. Had they

ever been inside? And, though most of them shared my enthusiasm over the possibilities the place conjured, none had the power or authority to save it. With Loany and Okie gone, Paradise Rice was really nothing more than a house—bricks and mortar and metal awnings, sitting vacant and deteriorating slowly away.

Then the summer Perry Rice died I learned his son Tom, (and Okie's grandson) just happened to drive by Paradise Rice as they were tearing it down. He spied two slot machines neatly stacked in the back of a pickup truck. I always knew they were there—never doubted it for one moment.

Okie the Goose outlived his namesake and still calls Circle S his home. Okie himself ended up making it a few months past his one hundredth birthday, and when he died, Loany pretty much died too, of a broken heart. A couple of days after his funeral, she suffered a stroke and was never quite the same. Yes, the twinkle in her eyes never faded, even after she lost most of her speech. *Most of her speech,* I might emphasize. Because, Loany never, ever lost her stunning command of profanity.

"Dammit. Shit," she spouted out in frustration, for not being able to will her mouth to say what her brain was thinking.

* * *

I smiled as I stood in the hallway of the nursing home after she died thinking back to my many visits with Loany.

The two of us laughed together as she cursed along, all annoyed that her mouth would not work.

"Why yes, Miss Leona did always cuss," the nursing home aide said. "Something fierce. She never lost that."

"Come here," the woman motioned up the hallway to the other aides. "This is Miss Leona's niece. She's telling stories." She turned back to me. "We all just loved Miss Leona. We aren't supposed to say this, you know, but she was our favorite."

Of course she was. She was everyone's favorite.

ACKNOWLEDGMENTS

Aristotle smartly noted that "the whole is greater than the sum of its parts". That notion has never been more evident to me than on this project. I could not have gone it alone, and for the journey so many others selflessly took with me, I whole heartedly thank you one and all.

First and foremost, I thank family members who so generously gave of their time, endured hours of interviews, and helped bring the Rices to life in those times before I was around.

A big thanks goes out to my parents, Ron and Ginny Hiermer, who enthusiastically embraced this project, provided me a sound foundation on all things Loany and Okie, and steered me toward all the right people.

To Patty Baugess, Rachael Baugess, Maxine Geddes, Betty and Boots Herriott, Jim and Sandy Karnes, and Perry and Kay Rice—you all are the kind of aunts, uncles, and cousins everyone should have in their life.

Special thanks to Marty and Jim Wilcox. You were cheering me on years before I put a pen to paper. I also thank Bill (Okie) Rice for his guitar composition and bringing us, "The Ballad of Okie and Leona." It's a fitting title to their special chapter.

I am especially indebted to a group of strangers who all became friends on this journey. Thanks to Robert Indian, Dick Sheets, Richard "Shep" Shepler, Ethel Sullivan, and Jackson Weaver.

Thanks also to Joe Mackall, writing mentor and author extraordinaire.

Thanks to my readers, Laura Huffman, Joan Uhley, Sue Pritchett, and Angelique Woods. I am truly fortunate for your enthusiastic assist. My gratitude also goes out to Doretta Thomas for "listening so well" to long distance readings.

To my posse at the Ohio Writers' Guild, I am grateful for your support, wisdom, wit, and careful critique. Special thanks go out to Rosalie Ungar and Clyde Henry for their mentorship and guidance.

Thanks to Kimberly Emery and Bill Weimer at Phantom Fireworks for their assistance in locating an authentic Chinese lantern firework digital image.

I thank Brad Pauquette and his entire team at Columbus Publishing Lab for their fantastic customer service and dedication in helping me meet a very tight book launch deadline.

To my editors, I am humbly indebted. I must recognize Carmen Ambrosio, whose copyedit of the first draft made it profoundly more polished and readable, and also prevented my fifth grade grammar teacher from haunting me from beyond the grave. To Carol Lynne, whose immense talent and thoughtful content review propelled this work to a higher level, I am indeed so grateful and lucky to have had you as my muse and guide. I thank you both for the care and heart you poured into this manuscript.

And finally, I thank Melissa Thomas, whose unending faith, encouragement, and support were the foundation upon which this book was written. You are always there to hold my umbrella, and for that I am truly blessed.

CPSIA information can be obtained
at www.ICGtesting.com
Printed in the USA
BVHW030308230719
554111BV00002B/218/P

9 780997 333404